Improving Early
Childhood Development

An Integrated Program
for the Philippines

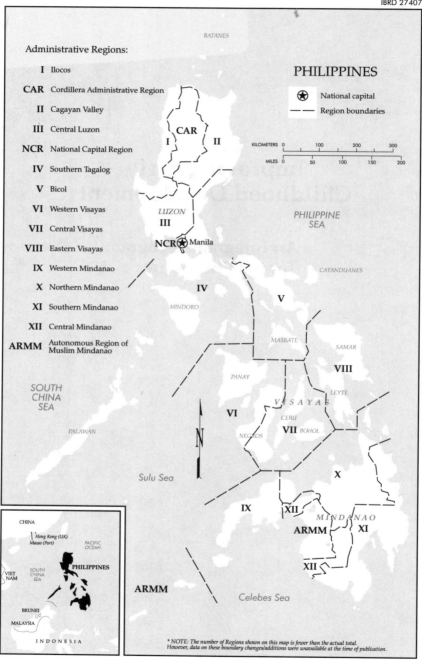

IBRD 27407

Administrative Regions:

I Ilocos

CAR Cordillera Administrative Region

II Cagayan Valley

III Central Luzon

NCR National Capital Region

IV Southern Tagalog

V Bicol

VI Western Visayas

VII Central Visayas

VIII Eastern Visayas

IX Western Mindanao

X Northern Mindanao

XI Southern Mindanao

XII Central Mindanao

ARMM Autonomous Region of Muslim Mindanao

PHILIPPINES

⊛ National capital

— — Region boundaries

KILOMETERS 0   100   200   300
MILES 0   50   100   150   200

BATANES

CAR

I   II

LUZON
III

NCR ⊛ Manila

PHILIPPINE SEA

CATANDUANES

IV

MINDORO

V

MASBATE   SAMAR

VIII

PANAY

VISAYAS   LEYTE

VI   CEBU

NEGROS   VII BOHOL

N

X

SOUTH CHINA SEA

PALAWAN

Sulu Sea

IX   XII   MINDANAO

ARMM   XI

XII

ARMM

Celebes Sea

CHINA

Hong Kong (UK)
Macao (Port)

PACIFIC OCEAN

VIET NAM   SOUTH CHINA SEA   PHILIPPINES

BRUNEI

MALAYSIA

INDONESIA

* NOTE: The number of Regions shown on this map is fewer than the actual total.
However, data on these boundary changes/additions were unavailable at the time of publication.

DIRECTIONS IN DEVELOPMENT

Improving Early Childhood Development

An Integrated Program for the Philippines

Richard A. Heaver
Joseph M. Hunt

*A collaborative report by the World Bank
and the Asian Development Bank for the
Government of the Republic of the Philippines*

The World Bank
Washington, D.C.

Contents

Foreword

This book is a joint product of the World Bank and the Asian Development Bank (ADB), and of a consultation process with key members of the child development community in the Philippines. It is based on a report that was produced to help in the preparation of a national investment plan for early childhood development (ECD). This is the first time either development bank has done a country study that looks at ECD in an integrated way, across health, nutrition, and early education. It is hoped, therefore, that this book will be of interest to the international child development community, as well as in the Philippines.

The first draft of the report was based on the findings of a joint mission in March 1994. Team members were Richard A. Heaver, IBRD (mission leader and management specialist); Joseph M. Hunt, ADB (ADB team leader and economist); ADB consultant Keith McInnes (financial analyst); and IBRD consultants Rosendo Capul (public health), Sony Chin (nongovernmental organizations and community participation), John Kevany (nutrition), and Fred Wood (early education). During this mission a workshop was held with leading specialists in child development in the Philippines, including governmental and nongovernmental organizations and the United Nations Children's Fund, to define the main issues on which the report should concentrate. A second workshop with similar participants was held in Manila in September 1994 to provide reactions to the first draft. Both workshops were chaired by the Philippine Council for the Welfare of Children. The current version of the report, on which this book is based, took into account comments from the second Manila workshop as well as comments by reviewers from inside and outside the World Bank at review meetings in Washington, D.C., in July and December 1994.

The broad findings of the report were endorsed by a steering committee—consisting of representatives of the main government agencies involved in ECD in the Philippines—that was tasked with developing a proposal for a national ECD program. Institutions represented on the steering committee include the Department of Health (chair); the National Council for the Welfare of Children; the National Nutrition Council; the Department of Social Welfare and Development; the Department of Education, Culture, and Sports; the Nutrition Center of the Philippines; the Department of Interior and Local Government; and the Museo Pambata Foundation. The findings helped the committee to prepare an ECD strategy paper for submission to the Social Development Committee, a high-level Philippine policymaking body, seeking endorsement of an integrated national ECD program. Although the report was broadly endorsed by the steering committee, the specific findings in this book and the levels of investment proposed represent the recommendations of the joint team, rather than the position of the government of the Philippines.

To provide a smaller, more accessible volume for the nontechnical reader, the eleven annexes to the report are being published in a separate companion volume, *Supplement to Improving Early Childhood Development.*

The authors gratefully acknowledge the contribution of all those in the Philippines and in the international agencies, as well as each member of the mission team, who provided data, shared their views about issues and priorities, and commented on drafts. Errors and omissions remain the responsibility of the authors alone.

Children represent the future of the nation. This book is dedicated to the many Filipinos who are working for the cause of children, in the hope that preschoolers, especially the disadvantaged, will have a better future.

Callisto E. Madavo
Director, East Asia and Pacific
Country Department I
The World Bank

Dinh X. Vinh
Director, Agriculture and
Social Services Department (East)
Asian Development Bank

Acronyms and Abbreviations

ABCSD	Area-Based Child Survival and Development
ADB	Asian Development Bank
ARMM	Autonomous Region of Muslim Mindanao
CAR	Cordillera Administrative Region
CODE-NGO	Caucus of Development NGO Networks
CWC	Council for the Welfare of Children
ECD	Early childhood development
EPI	Expanded Program on Immunization
FNRI	Food and Nutrition Research Institute
GDP	Gross domestic product
GMP	Growth monitoring and promotion
GNP	Gross national product
IALDM	Integrated Approach to Local Development Management
IEC	Information, education, and communication
IRA	Internal Revenue Allotment
IRS	International Reference Standard for Growth
NCR	National Capital Region
NEDA	National Economic and Development Authority
NGO	Nongovernmental organization
NNC	National Nutrition Council
ORT	Oral rehydration therapy
PEM	Protein-energy malnutrition
UNICEF	United Nations Children's Fund
USAID	U.S. Agency for International Development
WHO	World Health Organization

Glossary

Barangay The lowest level of local government, roughly equivalent to village; contains an average of 1,500 people (within a very wide range).

Municipality The local government level (both urban and rural) between a province and a barangay; contains an average of 20,000 people (within a very wide range).

Overview

The situation of children in the Philippines is considerably worse than it need be for a country of its per capita income. Ill health, malnutrition, and poor psychosocial development among pre-schoolers are costing the country substantial amounts in terms of premature deaths, permanent disabilities, and lost productivity and income. The benefits to the nation of improved child development greatly outweigh the costs. However, the benefits will arise over a long period, whereas making the investment in children is an immediate priority. The cost of inaction is high. Every year lost can be measured in deaths, disease, and often permanent disabilities.

This book argues that the Philippines should be investing more in child development and that doing so will have a high payoff. The objective is to convince those who control resources in the central and local governments, and in the nongovernmental and donor communities, that they should finance an integrated invest-ment package that has a real prospect of meeting the national goals for children. The technologies for program design and implementa-tion are well-enough known, the finance can be raised or reallo-cated, and the goals can be achieved—if the commitment of the government as well as the nongovernmental and donor communi-ties can be crystallized around a shared vision of what needs to be done.

The Situation of Preschool Children in the Philippines

Health

In the Philippines two of every three preschoolers who die are infants. The infant mortality rate is about 57 per 1,000 live births. During the 1980s the infant mortality rate declined much more slowly than in other East Asian countries. For example, although Thailand and the Philippines had similar infant mortality rates in the 1960s, Thailand's rate is now only about 30 per 1,000. The main

1

causes of infant and child deaths are pneumonia and other respiratory diseases; bronchitis, influenza, and diarrhea are the leading childhood diseases. Most of these deaths are preventable, and most of these diseases are treatable with cheap, simple technologies.

Child health has improved more slowly in the Philippines than elsewhere for a number of reasons. The deep economic recession and years of slow growth of the 1980s limited the access of the poor to public health services. Little was spent on the key primary technologies until the Aquino and Ramos governments came to power. Underinvestment in sectors outside child health, but which powerfully affect child health, also played an important part. Slow progress with the family planning program took a heavy toll in children's lives; it has been estimated that the infant and child mortality rates would decline by as much as 25 percent if pregnancy were avoided by women who are under 20 and over 45, women who have four or more children, and women who are within fifteen months of their last birth.

There was also underinvestment in controlling protein-energy malnutrition (PEM, which depresses the immune system; severe PEM can increase the risk of death by up to eight times. Recent research has shown that even moderate PEM, the degree of severity most common in the Philippines, is associated with increased disease and death rates; it is estimated that nearly half of infant and child deaths in the Philippines are the combined result of infection and malnutrition. Gains from further investment in child health programs may therefore be limited unless accompanied by equally determined efforts to improve nutrition.

Nutrition

The commonest form of malnutrition in the Philippines is iron deficiency anemia, which affects more than 40 percent of pregnant and lactating women and about 50 percent of infants. These levels may increase further once the new international standard for measuring anemia, recently adopted by the World Health Organization (WHO), has been adopted in the Philippines. This deficiency adversely affects children's growth and performance, including intellectual development. Iodine deficiency remains a serious problem in parts of the country, leading to cretinism, mental retardation, reduced learning capacity, and hearing loss in infants and children. Vitamin A deficiency is mostly now at subclinical levels, but even this remains a problem because of its recently discovered links with mortality. Micronutrient deficiencies result mainly from low dietary intakes: for anemia and vitamin A, through eating too few micronutrient-rich fruits and vegetables and, for iodine, because of geological conditions. Anemia is also exacerbated by iron loss caused by parasites—malarial, schistosomal, and helminthic—in ecological zones where these are prevalent.

During the 1980s, PEM declined more slowly in the Philippines than in not only the better-off countries of East Asia (Malaysia, Thailand) but also the poorer countries of South Asia (Bangladesh, India, Pakistan). Different kinds of standards are used to define the magnitude of PEM. By the Philippines Reference Standard, about 11 percent of children under 60 months old were underweight in 1992; by the International Reference Standard, endorsed by WHO, 33 percent were underweight. Using the International Reference Standard, which makes international comparisons possible, PEM in the Philippines in 1992 was worse than in poorer countries such as Egypt, Kenya, Tanzania, and Zimbabwe. Data from the 1993 Philippines National Nutrition Survey indicate that, by the Philippines Reference Standard, PEM had fallen to about 8 percent of children under age 6. This percentage would equate to about 29 percent by the International Standard. The continuing decline is encouraging, but the absolute amount remains a significant cause for concern.

PEM is often thought to result simply from poverty and lack of purchasing power for food. In the Philippines, household food insecurity affects 20 percent of families and is certainly an important factor in PEM. But so, also, are poor child health and poor caring practices for children. Wasting (low weight for height, which indicates current malnutrition) in preschoolers peaks between the ages of 6 months and 2 years and then, in most families with a nutrition problem, declines just when children are getting more expensive to feed. The peak around weaning reflects both the incidence of infection and inadequate weaning practices, even in families who can afford the food. It is likely that most mothers feed their children too little because they do not realize their children are malnourished; moderate PEM is not easily visible to the untrained eye. The multiple causes of PEM have important implications for policy. Many policymakers favor livelihood-creation programs as the solution for the nutrition problem. But investment in health care and efforts to improve caring practices are also essential. A key intervention is an effective program to monitor and promote growth. Such a program permits parents to recognize malnutrition and the positive effects of feeding affordable, additional amounts of food.

Early Education

There is very little survey data that directly measure children's psychosocial development. But indirect evidence from surveys of performance in elementary school is worrying. Although 99 percent of Filipino children are enrolled, dropout rates are unacceptably high. Only 68 percent of grade 1 entrants actually complete elementary school, with 60 percent of the dropout occurring in grades 1 and 2. Also, test results for those staying in school are lower than for other East Asian countries. It is not known how much of the dropout and poor learning performance should be attributed to poor school readiness, how much to poor teaching in elementary school, or how much to other factors. But high dropout rates and poor performance in school must be due in part to inadequate school readiness among Filipino children—readiness in their ability to deal with different ways of learning, their socialization with large groups of children their own age, and their language skills.

As noted above, persistent poor health and malnutrition are themselves important causes of inadequate psychosocial development. They can inhibit the development of intelligence and of neurological and psychomotor systems, and they make children less active and less responsive to stimulation. Other important influences are the amount of attention children receive from caregivers, the interaction they have with other children, and the richness of their environment. There is little solid data on any of these factors in the Philippines. In general, the families least likely to be able to provide for their children's developmental needs are the very poor, particularly those who have migrated to urban areas and are without extended family support systems to help with childcare. One study of women's work and infant care in Cebu showed that nearly 60 percent of mothers worked outside the home and that poor women with several preschoolers were the mothers most likely to be working outside the home.

The Worst-off

Depending on where they live and what type of family they come from, children are subject to different types and degrees of risk. Risk factors may be demographic (being an infant with closely spaced siblings), related to income (being the child of a poor, landless laborer), environmental (living in an area with malaria or unprotected water supplies), geographic (living in a mountain area or a coastal community only reachable by water), related to peace and order (being underprovided with services because of past armed conflict) or cultural (living in indigenous communities, which also have poor access to services). Families are worst-off usually because they suffer from combinations of such risks. In the Philippines, the worst-off areas in terms of high infant mortality and PEM rates are Bicol and Western Visayas; the best-off are the National Capital Region (NCR), Mindoro, and Region III in northern Luzon. But in terms of numbers of disadvantaged children, the picture is different: the worst-off include not only Western Visayas and Bicol, but also the NCR, Region I in northern Luzon, and Mindoro.

Implications for Action

To best design and target interventions, better data are needed in several areas. On the technical side, improvements are needed in disease surveillance and in measuring iron deficiency, PEM in pregnant and lactating women, and psychosocial development. For targeting purposes, better data are also needed on the most disadvantaged, including studies of their risk profiles, and better mechanisms are needed for identifying disadvantaged children scattered among populations of the better-off. Growth monitoring and household asset surveys appear to be cost-effective ways to collect these kinds of data.

The nature of child development problems in the Philippines suggests that the main priorities should be programs for:

- Child survival, with special attention to maintaining the Expanded Program on Immunization, acute respiratory infection control, oral rehydration therapy, and interventions aimed at neonatal mortality
- Disease control, with special attention to diarrhea and pneumonia nationally and to malaria, schistosomiasis, and helminth control in heavily endemic areas
- Deficiency control, for iron, vitamin A, and iodine among pregnant and lactating women as well as children
- PEM control, focusing on food security and behavioral change and on pregnant and lactating women as well as children
- Early education, for disadvantaged children (however, the lack of hard data makes it difficult to determine the appropriate extent and type of intervention)
- Maternal care and birth-spacing, aimed at improving mothers' health and nutrition and reducing infant and child mortality and malnutrition

- Water supply and sanitation, in areas where limited coverage leads to high diarrhea rates.

Government Policies, Goals, and Intervention Programs

The Philippines has a set of laws and policies, including a national Plan of Action for Children, that strongly support child development. The government's qualitative and quantitative goals for the survival, protection, and development of children are clear and ambitious. Between 1990 and 2000 the goal is to reduce the infant mortality rate to 37.6; to halve the prevalence of PEM among preschoolers; to reduce low birth weight to less than 10 percent; to virtually eliminate vitamin A and iodine deficiencies; and to establish a preschool center in every *barangay*.

To be most effective, early childhood development programs should attempt to integrate interventions in health, nutrition, and early education so as to respond to children's needs in a holistic way. Some of the strategy issues that cut across these three sectors are discussed in the following section. But first the existing programs in health, nutrition, and early education are reviewed separately because, until the recent devolution,[1] they have mainly been seen—and managed—as separate programs. Only the nationwide programs are reviewed, because the success or failure of these large-scale programs will determine whether the nation's child development goals are achieved. There are also a number of small-scale projects and programs in the Philippines that have attempted to integrate health, nutrition, and early education interventions and from which much can be learned about how to strengthen the national programs.

Health Programs

During 1991–93, health services were devolved to local governments. Now most of the hospitals are controlled by the seventy-seven provincial governments, and most public health services by the more than 1,500 municipalities. At the periphery, the key health worker is the rural health midwife, of which there is one for every 5,000 people on average, and one for every 2,000 to 3,000 people in most poorer provinces. Rural health midwives are assisted by barangay health workers. These volunteer workers help for two or three hours a week encouraging community participation in health campaigns and providing health education. A typical barangay of 1,500 people might have ten such volunteers, of whom half might be active workers.

The various child health programs have had different impacts, depending on the levels of commitment and funding they have had, how difficult their technology is to manage, and how long they have been established. The immunization program has been the most successful; strong commitment and ample funding have increased coverage to more than 90 percent. The diarrhea program has been the next most successful, with oral rehydration being used in 50 to 60 percent of cases. But more needs to be done to promote home prevention and management of diarrhea. The control of acute respiratory infections is a newer technology. This program was launched only five years ago. Much training has been done, but the current monitoring system has not been able to determine how far the new case management system is being followed in the field. Financing for expansion of the program is uncertain. Although support from the United Nations Children's Fund (UNICEF) will continue, assistance from the U.S. Agency for International Development (USAID) and the World Bank for acute respiratory infection control and other child survival interventions was scheduled to end in late 1994 or early 1995.

In contrast to the earlier, weak commitment to family planning, the Department of Health has now made the program for family planning, women's health, and safe motherhood its flagship program and is implementing two major, donor-supported projects to support it. Although efforts to improve and expand family planning should greatly affect infant mortality, more needs to be done to reduce the 35 percent of infant deaths that occur in the first month after birth.

With the government's increasing commitment to the child survival program and to women's health and family planning, the rural health midwife's workload is growing steadily. This increase implies the need to carefully review the ratio of field staff to population. It also implies the need for more systematic planning of the rural health midwife's time and the division of labor between her, the barangay health workers, and the doctors and nurses in the health centers. Efficiency would increase if fieldworkers' time were focused on providing integrated services to the clients who are most at risk and at the times when they most need assistance.

Except for interventions to reduce deaths in the first months of life, the technical strategies for child health interventions are well developed. The main constraints are institutional and financial. Since devolution there have been varying degrees of commitment and resource allocation, and at least in some local governments there are worrying signs that the delivery of public health services is beginning to falter. On the financial side, local governments inherited a series of child health programs that varied in their stage of development and effectiveness and still suffered from the legacy of underfunding of primary care during the 1980s. Substantial additional resources are required to consolidate these programs.

Nutrition Programs

At least eight agencies are involved in implementing nutrition programs. Foremost are the Department of Health and the Department of Social Welfare and Development. The Department of Health is responsible for the micronutrient program and for growth monitoring, as well as for nutrition education and supplementary feeding for pregnant and lactating women and children under age 4 (age 0 to 36 months). The Department of Social Welfare and Development runs a nutrition program, including supplementary feeding, for the 4- to 6-year-olds. At the periphery, the same rural health midwives and barangay health workers who are responsible for health are also responsible for nutrition. They are assisted by barangay nutrition scholars—volunteer workers with very small allowances (mostly not more than ₱50 [less than $2][2] a month) who work for one or two hours a day on growth monitoring, supplementary feeding, micronutrient distribution, and nutrition education. On average, there is one barangay nutrition scholar for every three barangays in the country.

The Department of Health, with good support from local governments, has launched major campaigns promoting vitamin A and iodine supplementation, and coverage rates are rising fast. Iron supplementation does not lend itself to the campaign approach for implementation because iron supplements have to be taken daily or weekly. The Department of Health therefore plans to improve the delivery of iron to pregnant women in the context of its women's health and safe motherhood program. Anemia also must be attacked through well-targeted efforts to control parasitic diseases, but more work is needed to define the areas of highest prevalence and to develop appropriate interventions.

Efforts to fortify staples with key micronutrients and to change dietary habits have moved less fast than supplementation interventions. Fortification has suffered from an ad hoc approach and would benefit from technical assistance to develop industrywide plans and the capacity to design, monitor, and evaluate the fortification program. The emerging overload on field staff, coupled with their inadequate training, is making it difficult to promote dietary change seriously.

Most cases of PEM in the Philippines are moderate rather than severe and hence not easily visible to the untrained eye. Growth monitoring is an essential tool for showing parents that their children are malnourished and that malnutrition responds quickly to feeding small additional quantities of food. For the same reason, short-term supplementary feeding of growth-faltering children is also useful. However, the growth promotion program in the Philippines has not worked well. Growth monitoring is often infrequent and of poor quality, as is counseling. Food supplementation has not been adequately targeted on the 0- to 24-month age group most at risk, food supplements for children are often taken home and shared with other family members, and many children stay in the feeding program for six to twenty-four months, thus encouraging dependency on it. There have been ambivalence and lack of understanding as to whether supplementation is a growth promotion intervention to educate parents about better childcare or a food security intervention to provide a safety net for the very poor.

Managing an effective growth promotion program focusing on children under 3 in a barangay of about 1,500 would take a worker four to six hours a day, six days a week. This kind of time commitment cannot be expected from volunteers. It is therefore recommended that a part-time community worker in each barangay be hired to run this program, with an allowance of about ₱750 ($27) a month. Existing barangay nutrition scholars could be used for the program where suitable.

The food supplementation program has depended heavily on U.S. Public Law 480 (PL 480) food aid, which is to be phased out in the next few years. We recommend that a suitable, locally produced weaning food be substituted for the PL 480 commodities and that the supplementation program be reoriented to focus on on-site feeding for at-risk pregnant women and 0- to 24-month-olds, the highest risk group.

A separate intervention will be required for families in which child malnutrition is the result of food insecurity rather than, or in addition to, poor health care and poor feeding practices. These families can be identified through household asset surveys, and the appropriate intervention will be an income supplementation program, such as food stamps or job creation through public works. At present the National Food Authority spends ₱2 billion[3] to ₱3 billion ($71 million to $107 million) a year to finance a generalized food subsidy, which has been shown to do little or nothing to improve the nutritional status of the poor. These funds would be better reallocated to finance effective growth promotion and food security programs of the above type.

In contrast to its commitment and initiative in micronutrient malnutrition, the government has mounted no comparable effort to improve the PEM control program. Despite a continuing reduction in PEM rates, moderate malnutrition, as measured by international standards, still affects more than a quarter of preschoolers. And given the close links between PEM and child deaths, continuing slow progress in reducing PEM may also threaten the achievement of national goals to reduce mortality. The proposed rapid phaseout of the PL 480 program will precipitate a reorientation of the nutrition program. It is essential to use this reform opportunity to redesign the nutrition program to benefit the most vulnerable: pregnant women and very young children. Reducing PEM will require not only livelihood-creation programs, as currently emphasized, but also a revamping of the growth promotion program and the creation of a new and more efficient, targeted food security intervention.

Early Education Programs

Before devolution the Department of Social Welfare and Development, through the Day Care Center Program, was the main government provider of early education services. As with health and nutrition programs, this program has now been devolved, and local governments are legally required to provide it. Although called a day care program, the Day Care Center Program is really a preschool program, because it takes children for only two to three hours a day. Its coverage has been expanding very rapidly, from 13,900 centers in 1991 to more than 18,000 in 1992, but the program still covers less than half of all barangays. The key peripheral worker is the day care worker, who is responsible for a day care center serving about sixty 4- to 6-year-old children in a barangay, about 45 percent of the population of that age group. Day care workers receive an allowance ranging from ₱500 to ₱1,000 ($18 to $36) a month and are supervised by social welfare workers at the municipal level.

In addition, the Department of Education, Culture, and Sports runs about 2,900 preschool classes for 6-year-olds, using its existing school buildings and teachers. (Elementary education in the Philippines has in the past not begun until age 7, but the government recently decided to extend entry to 6-year-olds.) The department has also recently allocated a small amount of money to begin a new community-based preschool program for 4- to 6-year-olds, bringing to the fore the question of how responsibility for early education should be divided between agencies. Given that the Department of Education, Culture, and Sports will be preoccupied with expanding elementary school and has no comparative pedagogical advantage in preschool, and given that the Department of Social Welfare and Development already has a very substantial preschool infrastructure, it seems sensible to upgrade the day care centers to become the national public sector preschool program for 3- to 5-year-olds.

It is generally agreed that the quality of the day care centers is low. Learning materials are in short supply, workers are generally poorly trained, and in some areas workers are not receiving a sufficient financial incentive for good-quality work. A variety of measures are needed to improve the program: improving curriculum content, developing minimum acceptable standards for a day care center, creating a new training capacity, raising day care workers' allowances where these are less than ₱1,000 ($36) a month, limiting the number of children in each class to no more than twenty, and adding a social welfare worker in each municipality to ensure good-quality supervision and on-the-job training. To increase the outreach and equity of the program, satellite home-based centers, serving six or seven children, could be developed where poor clients live outside easy reach of the village center.

It is difficult to assess how effective the operation of the early education program is because systematic evaluation is not taking place. This situation needs to be remedied as a priority. But it is clear that the quality is low and that most local governments are preoccupied with expanding the number of centers rather than making them work well. If the quality is to be improved, local governments will have to have an assistance package in which the local government would undertake to improve quality according to measures that have been agreed on in return for technical, financial, and training assistance from the Department of Social Welfare and Development.

Strategy Issues

This section begins by summarizing some technical, institutional, and financial issues that are specific to nutrition and to early education. The subsequent issues—the overriding ones in child development—all relate to how the government can integrate what is now essentially a series of vertical interventions into a child development program that responds to the needs of the child as a whole. Cross-cutting issues include how to target the most disadvantaged and provide integrated services to them, how to maximize the contribution of local communities and nongovernmental organizations to the program, and how to manage the program under devolution.

Strategies for Reducing PEM

As noted above, the current nutrition strategy has not reduced moderate malnutrition to acceptable levels. Several changes in strategy appear to be required. First, the growth promotion program at the barangay level seems unlikely to succeed unless nutrition workers are better trained and paid a financial incentive commensurate with the time it takes to do good growth monitoring, counseling, and supplementary feeding for a large population of malnourished mothers and children. Second, with the phasing out of PL 480 resources, the government will need to take financial responsibility for the supplementary feeding program. Furthermore, it will need to retarget the feeding program to the neediest women and children to make sure the additional expenditure is used as efficiently as possible. Third, the growth promotion program will need to be complemented by an effective nutrition safety net program for the food insecure, perhaps through a food stamp or public works program.

These three changes will together require a significantly increased financial commitment to the nutrition program. Such a commitment is affordable for a country with the Philippines' per capita income; poorer countries such as India have already been able to put national PEM programs with similar strategies and financial requirements into place. Nevertheless, putting additional resources into the PEM program will be difficult, given the current fiscal constraints. Because the government is already spending, unproductively, an amount on a generalized food subsidy that would be enough to finance the recurrent costs of reorienting the PEM program along the above lines, the most efficient financing option would be to reallocate resources currently going to the National Food Authority.

The Government's Role in Early Education

Although the government's role in financing a minimum package of health and nutrition services is well accepted in the Philippines, its financing role in early education is more controversial. The key issues center on the role of government in early education and day care—the areas that involve significant capital and recurrent costs. Data on the cost-effectiveness of preschooling in the Philippines are very weak. A recent study concluded that preschooling reduces the dropout rate from school and improves the performance of those who stay in school. But the study did not look at the cost or quality of the existing system or analyze the relative cost-effectiveness of different approaches. Given the uncertainties about relative cost-effectiveness and the best way to design a preschool program in the Philippines, we conclude that not enough is known for the government to fund a program of universal preschooling. To determine whether the government should do so, a longitudinal cost-effectiveness study of different approaches to preschooling should be undertaken.

Despite uncertainties about funding universal preschooling, a case can be made for the government to improve the quality and coverage of the existing day care center program, provided that the most disadvantaged children in each barangay get access to the program and that the day care center become a convergence point for all early childhood development (ECD) services in the barangay and hence be used to maximize the synergy of health, nutrition, and education interventions. The poor cannot afford to send their children to private sector preschools. But the study of preschooling mentioned above did unambiguously show that going to preschool reduces the likelihood of poor children dropping out of elementary school to the point where they are no more likely to do so than the children of the better-off. From an equity perspective, an already mandated intervention that significantly narrows the differential between poor and rich should receive continued public sector support until there is hard evidence that an alternative approach is more cost-effective.

The situation with regard to day care for the children of working mothers is different. Here the potential role for the private sector is much greater. In addition to providing long-term benefits to society, day-long day care (as opposed to the two to three hours of preschool offered by the so-called day care program) offers immediate financial benefits to parents because it frees their time to enter the labor market or to take a higher-paying job outside the home. Private sector, home-based day care has been shown in other countries to be both financially viable and equitable; low overheads mean that the service is affordable even for poor women, and the centers themselves generate additional employment for poor women. But this system is not yet widespread in the Philippines. Therefore a case can be made for the government to provide seed money and technical support for demonstration home-based day care centers so that poor women are aware that they can be both users and providers of the service.

Targeting Field Services

The government has ranked provinces in terms of disadvantage using a weighted indicator that includes measures of illiteracy, infant mortality, malnutrition, sanitation, and the head count and poverty gap definitions of poverty. This mechanism for geographic targeting is proposed as the main way to allocate additional resources for antipoverty programs. But, as noted above, many disadvantaged children in better-off regions of the country, such as the National Capital Region and Mindoro, will be neglected if this targeting mechanism is applied to the ECD program. Thus the government should adopt alternative targeting mechanisms that are able to select the most disadvantaged and the most at risk from among populations of the better-off throughout the country.

Given the difficulties of using income as a targeting mechanism, and given that low income often inadequately predicts which families will have an at-risk child, a two-step, non-income-based targeting mechanism should be used. The first step identifies those women in each barangay who are pregnant or lactating, as well as all children under 6, as the members of the population who are at the most vulnerable period of the reproductive cycle from a developmental perspective. This would be the broad target group on which fieldworkers should concentrate their time. The second step identifies families within this group that are actually or potentially most at risk by measuring PEM status and family assets as proxies for the whole range of indicators of disadvantage.

The Convergence of Field Services

Evidence from around the world clearly shows that ECD programs that integrate health, nutrition, and early education interventions have more impact than those aimed at one aspect of child development alone. This is because disadvantage in one aspect of development reinforces disadvantage in another (Box 1). Children who are malnourished are more likely to fall ill, and vice versa. And children who are malnourished or ill learn more slowly. The mutually reinforcing nature of child development problems means that integrated programs benefit greatly from synergy. Strategies to ensure the convergence of services in the field assume particular importance in this context.

Box 1. Interrelation of Health, Nutrition, and Education on Early Childhood Development

Health impacts on nutrition

- Severe or multiple acute respiratory infections and fevers lead to weight loss.
- Severe or repeated diarrhea and associated dehydration reduce nutrient uptake and lead to weight loss.
- Heavy parasite loads (intestinal, malarial, schistosomes) reduce nutrient uptake.

Nutrition impacts on health

- Children not eating enough have weakened immune systems and are more likely to get infections and die.
- Vitamin A–deficient children also have weakened immune systems and are more likely to be ill and die.

Health and nutrition impacts on psychosocial development and learning

- Children with iodine deficiency have lower IQs.
- Malnourished and frequently ill preschoolers are listless, play less, learn less at home, and become less well socialized.
- Malnourished and frequently ill children have poor school attendance and are more likely to drop out.
- Malnourished children have shorter attention spans and less learning capacity in class.

Preschool impacts on school

- Children who have been to an organized preschool are better socialized and adjust more quickly to elementary school.
- Children who have attended preschool are likely to progress more quickly and achieve better test results, particularly in the early primary grades.
- Children who have attended preschool are less likely to drop out in the course of primary school.

Because of devolution, and for the first time, the key ECD workers at the barangay level now all report to one authority at the city or municipal level. Advantage needs to be taken of this new opportunity to integrate services. In the past, the delivery of ECD services was split among several agencies, and heavy reliance had to be placed on interagency committees to coordinate the integration of services. Interagency committees are a relatively weak mechanism for changing the behavior of workers in the field. Now that the management of service delivery for all ECD interventions is integrated at the local government level, the convergence of services can be approached through the more effective mechanism of redesigning both the job content of workers at the periphery and the way in which supervision and on-the-job training are carried out.

The job content of the proposed new child development worker for children under age 4 and of the existing day care worker should be designed so that each can provide the full range of core ECD services appropriate for the age group for which the worker is responsible. In practice, because children's needs are different at different ages, the child development worker would spend more time on health and nutrition, and the day care worker would spend more time on organized preschool activities. Much could also be done to integrate supervision and training: redesign supervision routines so that health, nutrition, and social welfare staff make some joint visits and attend staff meetings together; develop a common core curriculum for training child development workers and day care workers; and have an integrated team of health, nutrition, and social welfare staff provide training.

Participation by Communities and Nongovernmental Organizations

For communities and nongovernmental organizations (NGOs), participation in development programs can vary from simple consultation, through involvement in program monitoring, to full-scale program management. A systematic process of consulting with disadvantaged communities, using structured interviews and focus groups, needs to be set up, preferably using the skills of NGOs that have the confidence of client communities. These consultations should be used to gain a better picture of communities' preferences and needs and to develop options for ECD programs appropriate for different circumstances. Also, communities and NGOs could be given a greater role in monitoring programs. For example, they could post key program performance information at day care centers. And communities could be involved in "verbal autopsies"—inquiries into what went wrong with the ECD program in the event of a preventable child death.

Government funds should also be used to finance ECD interventions jointly planned and managed by local governments, community organizations, and NGOs along the lines of the Community Health Partnerships already set up by the Department of Health. Where experienced NGOs exist and can help intermediate between local governments and communities, these partnerships are likely to be the best mechanism for developing the Child Development Program Agreements proposed below and for ensuring that they reflect local priorities. Outstanding NGOs could also greatly increase their impact if given more opportunities to leverage their resources and expertise by helping other institutions expand and improve their quality. They could help in consultations with local governments and communities; with curriculum development and training; with experimenting with and evaluating different ways to deliver services, especially in early education; with developing the institutional capacity of other NGOs; and with policy analysis and evaluation.

The for-profit NGO sector is most active in preschool education. The Department of Education, Culture, and Sports has accredited more than 1,300 private preschools, and it is believed there may be several times that number of small, unaccredited preschools and day care centers. The government's main current involvement is with accreditation. A more proactive role is recommended, including experimentation with technical assistance and training to improve the quality of private preschools and, more radically, with financing private sector preschools on a contract basis. But the cost-effectiveness of private sector support and provision needs to be carefully evaluated before applying such approaches nationwide.

Program Management under Devolution

Most provincial and municipal governments took over child development and other social services with very little experience in how to manage them. There are few data as yet on how they have performed or how spending behavior in the social sectors has changed. However, there is some concern that public demand for clinical care and new day care centers may cause priorities to shift at the expense of outreach care and program quality. The central government is also having to adapt to a new role—that of not managing, but influencing, program implementation. This is done through "marketing" priority programs, providing technical assistance, and using central financing to supplement and influence the use of local government resources.

Both the Department of Health and the Department of Social Welfare and Development need to develop their capacity to advocate child development to local governments and to systematically consult them about their priorities. In training, the Department of Social Welfare and Development in particular, as a small agency, needs to build up its institutional capacity to support local governments. In financing, the Department of Health has developed the concept of Comprehensive Health Care Agreements, in which local governments agree to provide certain services in return for specified hardware, cash, and software from the national government. It would be desirable for the Department of Social Welfare and Development to adopt a similar mechanism and to form with the Department of Health and local governments joint "Child Development Program Agreements" that would govern all investment in ECD in an integrated way.

The Role of the Central Support Institutions

The Council for the Welfare of Children is the main agency for formulating policy on, coordinating, and monitoring child development. A fairly new and very small agency with a budget of only P5 million ($0.18 million) in 1994, the council has few highly skilled technical personnel and limited influence with the cabinet and line agencies when it comes to budgets for child development programs. For the council to become a fully effective national oversight agency for children, its structure needs to be reviewed, the number and levels of professional posts increased, and its budget increased substantially.

The National Nutrition Council's staff is more than three times as large as that of the Council for the Welfare of Children, but it, too, because of its advisory status, has had difficulty in influencing policies and budgets. And although it has done much useful research, it has not rigorously analyzed some of the key issues, such as what causes malnutrition in the Philippines and whether expenditures from the generalized food subsidy should be reallocated into an effective program to both promote growth and provide a safety net. A key issue with regard to the National Nutrition Council is whether it should develop a comparative advantage in one or two major missions or continue with its multiple missions, which now include policy analysis and development; program coordination; nutrition surveillance; information, education, and communication; and coordination of the implementation of certain intervention programs.

Finally, early education has no national support institution comparable to those already established in health and nutrition. Consideration needs to be given as to whether a new institution should be created for this purpose. Given the government's lack of comparative advantage in early education, and given existing moves to streamline the civil service, it may be preferable to support early education by establishing a network of existing governmental and nongovernmental institutions with expertise in this area. This network would need a small secretariat that would provide direction and guidance and that would have a discretionary budget allowing it to commission work from qualified network members.

Financing a Strengthened ECD Program

The budget for ECD programs in 1994 was approximately ₱2,107 million ($84 million), or about ₱195 ($7.80) for each preschooler. Allocations to ECD need to rise substantially to meet the gaps in coverage and quality noted above. However, unless policy action is taken, allocations for ECD will probably fall by as much as half a billion pesos (about $18 million) rather than rise. Unless other resources can be found to substitute for the ₱430 million ($15 million) PL 480 spending on food supplements, the current amount spent on nutrition will fall by about half. If the apparently exceptional ₱91 million ($3.26 million) 1994 congressional insertion for the day care center program is not sustained, the amount spent on early education may also fall. The 1995 budget included ₱63 million ($2.26 million) for the day care program, a reduction of almost one third. As a congressional initiative, there is no guarantee that this item will be renewed annually. This would reduce spending to about ₱150 ($5.90) per child.

On the basis of assumptions detailed in the following chapters, the cost of bringing the national ECD program up to a level of quality and coverage sufficient to meet national targets would be ₱9.6 billion to ₱10.5 billion ($342 million to $374 million) over six years. Table 1 shows the breakdown of these costs, assuming

Table 1. Estimated Costs, Available Resources, and Financing Gap for Investments in Early Childhood Development Programs over Six Years in the Philippines
(millions of pesos)

	Health	Nutrition	Education	Total
Total costs	7,128	6,793	4,937	18,857
Available resources	4,433	2,951	1,451	8,835
Resources as a percentage of costs	62	43	29	47
Financing gap	2,695	3,842	3,486	10,023
Financing gap (millions of dollars)	96	137	124	358

Source: World Bank and ADB data.

investment in the middle of this range. It indicates that, overall, the resources currently planned for ECD are about 47 percent of what is needed. These estimates are conservative in that they assume a fairly modest, even phasing of program expansion over six years.

At the time of devolution, local governments inherited an unfinished agenda for ECD, an agenda that required substantial additional investment. The revenues that provinces and municipalities were allotted then and their revenue growth since are insufficient to strengthen and expand the program. Although local governments and local communities should pay their share, it is clear that the central government will need to provide continuing financial support for ECD activities, as it does in other countries. However, the central government must also avoid simply substituting its financing for efforts that local governments could otherwise make. This implies that a cost-sharing policy be developed. Such a policy should ensure that local governments increase their share of ECD program financing over time as their revenues and their ability to sustain the ECD program increase. At the same time the policy should ensure that the central government continue to partly finance the ECD program, if necessary, over the long term in municipalities whose weak revenue base, large populations, and poor ECD indicators make it impossible to sustain the program alone. Developing an appropriate cost-sharing policy will require the collection of additional data on local governments' ability and willingness to pay for ECD programs. Collecting these data is a high priority.

The incremental recurrent cost required to sustain a strengthened and expanded ECD program would be in the range of ₱1.5 billion to ₱2 billion ($54 million to $71 million) a year over five to ten years. It is now not clear how much of this the local governments could finance. On the central government side, much of the Department of Health's requirement could be met from the proposed allocation for ECD in its investment plan. But the Department of Social Welfare and Development would require an increased ceiling to fund a strengthening of the day care program. Reallocating resources within and between government departments could free up substantial additional funds for ECD if this program is designated as a national priority. With the upcoming reduction in PL 480 support, a particularly strong case can be made for reallocating food subsidy expenditures made by the National Food Authority into an effective nutrition program for children. However, budget reallocations are politically difficult and take time. Time is also required for local government revenues to grow to a point where local governments can sustain an increasing share of the ECD program. In the interim, foreign aid could help to fill the financing gap. The donor community is putting few resources into ECD; a strong case could be made for donors to substantially increase their commitments if the government decides that reorienting and strengthening the ECD program is a national priority.

The Returns to Investment

The kinds of primary care interventions in health and nutrition included in the Philippines ECD program rank among the most cost-effective of all health interventions. Global estimates indicate that the equivalent of an extra year of healthy life can be obtained by spending $25 to $30 on immunization, vitamin A, and iodine supplementation or about $63 on food supplementation. For comparison, prenatal and delivery care cost $60 to $110 and family planning $100 to $150 for each healthy life-year gained. These ECD interventions are not only quite cheap to implement, but also save later government expenditure on much more expensive hospital care and rehabilitation. And they are good for equity, because the children of the poor suffer disproportionately from ill health and malnutrition.

A recent computer simulation of the impact of improving child malnutrition in the Philippines indicated significant potential benefits. It estimated that a 50 percent reduction in PEM would avert more than 37,000 infant and child deaths each year and save 150 million to 200 million days of illness each year. Reducing iodine deficiency by half would avert more than 15,000 cases of mental retardation every year. Reducing anemia by half might lead to additional earnings from increased agricultural productivity of more than ₱1,340 million ($48 million) a year. And reducing iron deficiency, stunting (low height for age, which indicates cumulative malnutrition over time), and malnutrition-related mortality by half might lead to additional wage earnings of ₱8,400 million ($300 million) a year.

Quantifying the cost-effectiveness of preschool is more difficult. But it is clear that integrated interventions in health, nutrition, and early education reduce the school dropout rate and improve children's performance in school. There is also evidence that integrated ECD programs have sustained long-term benefits to the economy and society. Evaluation of a U.S. ECD program for disadvantaged inner city children that has run since 1962 showed that for every dollar invested, $7 was gained in lower expenditures on education and welfare and higher productivity among participants. At age 19, former participants were 56 to 80 percent more likely to be literate, enrolled in postsecondary education, or employed and 39 to

57 percent less likely to be classified as mentally retarded, school dropouts, arrested for criminal activity, or on welfare.

Recommendations

A serious effort to improve the situation of preschoolers would require a commitment to the following four policies.

- *Move from a system of largely separate, vertical programs to an integrated program approach to health, nutrition, and early education.* Because of the synergy among investments in each of these areas, an integrated approach will mean more benefit for each peso invested. Effective integration will require significant institutional changes (see Box 4-1 for a summary).
- *Mount a determined drive to improve the quality of programs.* Among other things, this effort will require increased staffing levels to realistically reflect workloads for service delivery and for support and supervision. In particular, a paid worker is needed in each disadvantaged barangay to look after the ECD needs of pregnant and lactating women, as well as children under 4. Also, additional supervisors are needed for the day care program because the ratio of supervisors to day care workers is inadequate for good-quality supervision and on-the-job training.
- *Substantially increase spending on ECD, to increase both the quality of programs and their coverage to unserved, disadvantaged children.* The Philippines is now spending about ₱195 ($7.80) per preschooler on ECD—an amount that with current plans will fall during the next few years to about ₱150 ($5.90) as existing child survival projects come to an end and donor support for the PL 480 nutrition program is phased out. Instead of allowing resources for children to fall, during the next six years the government should be investing about ₱275 ($11) per child—an increase of about 40 percent—to achieve the national goals for children. The total required increment over the six years is estimated to be about ₱10 billion ($400 million). Much of this increment could be met by reallocating resources now spent less productively. In particular, funds for food subsidies from the National Food Authority, which appear to have little impact on malnutrition, could be much more productively spent on a targeted nutrition program for preschoolers.
- *Accept that achieving the nation's ECD goals will require a sustained investment by the public sector in recurrent costs over the*

medium and long terms. More than 80 percent of the estimated six-year investment requirements represent recurrent costs. Some of this investment can come from local governments; an urgent priority is to collect data on local governments' ability and willingness to pay for ECD services so that an equitable cost-sharing policy between the central and local governments can be determined. But many areas in the country where children are worst-off are also those where local governments are least able to pay for improved and expanded services. Here the central government will need to make a policy commitment to partly finance the recurrent costs of strengthening the ECD program over the medium and long terms. This kind of investment is amply justified in cost-benefit terms and on the grounds of equity and market failure.

If these general commitments are made, the central government would need to take the following steps to translate policy intentions into a program of action:

Preparation Phase

- Resolve specific policy issues relating to the current nutrition and early education programs and to the appropriate form of central technical support for child development in general and early education in particular
- Develop a detailed, costed child development program plan, in consultation with local communities and local governments
- Mount studies on local governments' ability and willingness to pay for ECD, as a prelude to developing cost-sharing policies between central and local government.

Implementation Phase

- Rapidly implement interventions where it is clear what needs to be done (for example, expand health and nutrition programs and strengthen the existing day care program)
- Do pilots of interventions where the best approaches to implementation are unclear (for example, pilot home-based day care centers)
- Initiate research studies where the appropriateness, scale, or type of public sector intervention is unclear (for example, research whether the government should provide preschooling for children of the better-off).

Notes

1. Devolution is an extreme form of decentralization. It involves not only increasing the responsibilities of lower levels of government but also transferring substantial budgetary control to them. The Philippine government devolved a number of services, including health, social welfare, and agricultural extension, in 1991.

2. All dollar amounts are in 1994 U.S. dollars, with no allowance for inflation.

3. A billion is 1,000 million.

1. Introduction

This study appears to be the first in the Philippines to attempt a comprehensive, combined review of the three subsectors—health, nutrition, and education—that most affect the development of preschool children. Because this book presents a broad sectoral review rather than a project proposal, it aims to provide no more than an overview of the problems, issues, and needed interventions in early childhood development. To turn the general recommendations and estimates made here into a detailed, costed investment program requires more work.

In line with its broad scope, the intended audience of this book is the whole community of those involved in planning, managing, and financing child development in the Philippines. This includes the agencies of the central government with policy responsibility for early childhood development; the politicians and economic agencies at the national level who allocate resources; the local governments, which are now both financiers and implementors of the program; the nongovernmental organizations involved in program implementation, advocacy, or technical support; and the foreign aid community.

This book has three specific objectives. The first is to inform. Many of those involved in child development are well informed on the program with which they are immediately concerned but less well informed on other programs equally important to the development of the child. Others have developed effective, integrated services on a small scale but lack the big picture of what is happening nationally. The hope is that a shared vision of problems and needs in the sector will lead to unified action.

The second objective is to review and analyze. The book attempts to go beyond a situation analysis of the status of children and to form some judgments about the effectiveness of the main national programs and the needs for reorientation and investment. In particular, the book analyzes what causes protein-energy malnutrition (PEM) and what an appropriate response to the problem might be. This analysis goes beyond the conventional wisdom that PEM is a problem of poverty and lack of purchasing power. The book also presents an analysis of sectoral resource needs, an analysis that, although approximate, goes beyond what has been done before in both scope and detail.

The third objective is to advocate. The book argues that the Philippines should be investing more in child development and that doing so will have a high payoff. The objective is to convince those who control resources in the central and local governments, and in the nongovernmental and donor communities, that they should finance an integrated investment package that has a real prospect of meeting the national goals for children. The technologies for program design and implementation are well-enough known; the finance can be raised or reallocated; and the goals can be achieved—if the commitment of the government, nongovernmental, and donor communities can be crystallized around a shared vision of what needs to be done.

This chapter summarizes what is meant by child development, as opposed to just child survival—which was until recently the main objective of programs for children—and what the main characteristics of an effective early childhood development (ECD) program are. It also reviews the growing body of evidence showing that government investment in child development, in addition to being a humanitarian priority, has a high economic payoff.

Chapter 2 summarizes the data on the developmental status of preschool children in the Philippines, focusing on which children are the most disadvantaged. It offers suggestions for improving the quality and usefulness of the data and draws implications from the data about the kinds of programs that would have the most impact on the development and welfare of young children.

Chapter 3 reviews the coverage and quality of the current programs in each subsector—health, nutrition, and early education— to determine which strategies are sound and which need substantial reorientation if national goals are to be met.

Chapter 4, in contrast to Chapter 3, takes a cross-sectoral perspective. It looks at ways to integrate the interventions and reviews issues common to all three programs, such as how best to manage them now that responsibility for implementation has devolved to local governments and how best to maximize the participation of communities and NGOs.

Finally, Chapter 5 looks at the key financing issues in the sector: how much the Philippines has invested compared with other Asian countries; the additional resources required to reach national goals;

and the prospects for financing and sustaining the additional investment required.

What Is Early Childhood Development?

During the 1970s and much of the 1980s, the aim of large-scale investment in programs to assist children in the developing world was mainly child survival. By contrast, the aim of child development programs is not only to promote survival but also to promote the physical, intellectual, social, and emotional development of those who survive, recognizing that children cannot develop fully as personalities or contribute fully to society unless attention is paid to all these aspects of development. Such programs often focus on early childhood, that is, the preschool years, because this is the period when children develop fastest and a good deal of research shows that, if children's development is compromised at this stage, it is often impossible, and always much more difficult and expensive, to compensate for the disadvantage later.

In this book, child development problems refer to problems of ill health, malnutrition, or inadequate psychosocial development, the last being used as a summary term for intellectual, social, and emotional development. Child development interventions mean health, nutrition, and early education interventions, with the understanding that early education in this field means not just organized education, such as nursery school or kindergarten, but everything that parents do to provide an intellectually stimulating, socially adjusting, and emotionally supportive environment for their children. The book deals only with early childhood development (or ECD), that is, with the development of preschoolers, although for convenience ECD is often referred to simply as child development.

The concept of a child development program is not universally familiar. The remainder of this section, therefore, discusses how interest in early childhood development evolved and what kinds of activities are seen as the essential ingredients of an effective child development program.

The Evolution of Interest

At least three factors are responsible for the rising interest in child development during the past ten years. The first is simply the increasing success of child survival programs, coupled with progress in economic development. As infant and child death rates have fallen, especially in Latin America and Asia, governments have been less overwhelmed with the emergency of survival; at the same time, rising incomes and bigger government budgets have allowed them to think of expenditures beyond those for survival.

A second factor has been a wave of research findings, some of which are summarized below, showing not only that investment in child development has high economic returns but also that failure to invest in child development results in reduced school performance, a less productive labor force, and increased welfare and other social expenditures.

A third factor has been a succession of international events that have done much to promote these research findings and the importance of child development generally. These include the conferences prior to the adoption of the 1989 Convention on the Rights of the Child; the 1990 World Summit for Children, at which a number of ambitious development goals were adopted; the 1990 World Conference on Education for All, which, under the slogan "learning begins at birth," affirmed the importance of early education for later development; and the 1992 International Conference on Nutrition, at which participants committed their governments to achieving substantial reductions in child malnutrition. Largely because of the leadership of UNICEF at these conferences and elsewhere, child development has moved from UNICEF's advocacy agenda to become part of the mainstream development agenda of most governments and foreign aid agencies.

As of the mid-1990s, progress in child development around the world is very mixed. Some countries made major financial commitments to launching and expanding child development programs in the early 1980s. India, whose Integrated Child Development Services program now covers most of the country's most disadvantaged children, is an example of what can be achieved despite low per capita income. Other countries, including the Philippines, have pledged their political commitment to child development in international fora but have yet to translate their pledge into a financial commitment sufficient to achieve the ambitious goals they set themselves at the World Summit.

Designing Effective ECD Programs

From research findings and field experience with intervention programs, a good deal is now known about what makes an ECD program effective. Four design features in particular stand out and may be taken as prescriptive. We discuss them below; they are discussed more fully, together with others, in Myers (1992), a seminal reference that sets out the current "state of the art" in child development.

FOLLOW AN INTEGRATED APPROACH. Effective ECD programs combine interventions in health, nutrition, and early education. The cross-sectoral approach is advocated partly because this makes sense to parents and children. "A child is born without barriers. Its needs are integrated, and it is we who choose to compartmentalize them into health, nutrition, or education. Yet the child itself cannot isolate its hunger for food from its hunger for affection or its hunger for knowledge" (Alva 1986 quoted in Myers 1992).

A combined approach also has more impact. Disadvantage in one aspect of development reinforces a child's disadvantage in others. For example, children who are malnourished are more likely to fall ill, and vice versa; and children who are malnourished or ill learn less quickly. Box 1-1 sets out several of the most important linkages between health, nutrition, and psychosocial development. A child's risks of death or disadvantage combine geometrically rather than arithmetically. That is, a child who is severely malnourished as well as ill has not just twice but several times the risk of dying that a child who is only ill does. The mutually reinforcing nature of health, nutrition, and psychosocial developmental problems means that, correspondingly, integrated approaches to solving them benefit from synergy and have a much higher payoff than projects or programs aimed at one aspect of child development alone.

Integrating health, nutrition, and early education efforts at the operational level does not necessarily imply that management has to be integrated. Child development interventions in different sectors do not have to be implemented under the aegis of a single organizational structure in order to achieve effective integration in their effects. Although an integrated structure may be best in theory, radically altering existing organizational arrangements may entail adverse political or other consequences and can dissipate energy better directed at helping the children. Therefore, depending on the situation, organizing services from different agencies so that they converge on families in need in a coordinated manner may be more practical than integration in the strict sense.

BEGIN BEFORE BIRTH AND ADOPT DIFFERENT INTERVENTIONS AT DIFFERENT AGES. Most of the development of a child's brain, nervous system, and motor system is complete by the age of 6; much of

---

Box 1-1. Benefits of Early Childhood Development Programs

Sectoral benefits

- Health: Cost-benefit advantages of health interventions targeted on children
    Lower mortality
    Lower morbidity
    Lower costs of care
    Lower permanent disabilities

- Nutrition: Cost-benefit advantages of nutrition interventions targeted on children
    Lower mortality
    Lower morbidity
    Lower costs of rehabilitation
    Lower permanent disabilities

- Early education: Cost-benefit advantages of early childhood education
    Fuller physical, intellectual, social, and emotional development

Benefits from integration

- Cost-benefit advantages of combining health, nutrition, and early education interventions (achieving more together than if each were done alone)

Equity-related benefits

- Cost-benefit advantages relating to targeting interventions to the most disadvantaged
- Increased benefits from other existing investments
- Cost-benefit advantages from making other human resource investments more productive (for example, making the very large sunk costs in the school system more productive)

---

it is accomplished by the age of 2; and, if it can be said that "learning begins at birth," then it also can be said that good health and nutrition begin in the womb. Child development interventions must therefore attend to the health and nutritional status of the mother as early as possible during pregnancy, because this determines the health and nutrition of the fetus. Research evidence also shows that micronutrient or protein-energy malnutrition, if not prevented or corrected by the age of 2 or 3, is impossible or very difficult and expensive to correct later. Early intervention of the right type is crucial.

ECD interventions also need to vary in response to the child's differing needs at different ages. For example, a child's psychosocial developmental needs are very different as an infant, as a toddler, and as a four-year-old. Infants need body contact with the parent, good feeding practices, and appropriate stimulation. Toddlers are exploring a wider environment and need quite different kinds of attention and opportunities for learning. The developmental needs of a 4-year-old can no longer be fully met by the immediate family; the child's social and emotional development will be inhibited if he or she does not learn to interact with children of a similar age.

AIM AT FAMILIES, NOT JUST CHILDREN. ECD programs should try to increase the capacity of families to provide for the development of their own children rather than simply correct whatever disadvantage a child is currently suffering from. The programs need to aim particularly at mothers, both because the mother's health and nutrition during pregnancy determine the child's health and nutrition at birth and because mothers are the primary providers of care to preschoolers. But the programs must also look at the family as a unit, because a child's advantages or disadvantages stem from the situation of the family as a whole. Also, not just mothers but often fathers, grandparents, and siblings care for and influence the child.

To be effective, child development workers must be drawn from the local community so that they have easy access to their clients, know them well, and are trusted by them. The client load must be sufficiently small to allow for thorough communication and education—a precondition of program effectiveness. In Chapter 3 we discuss what a realistic client load is and how this would affect staffing requirements.

FOSTER PARTICIPATION. Just as ECD programs should empower the family to meet the child's full developmental needs, so should they empower the community to provide for the welfare of all of its children. Well-designed programs therefore foster the participation of the clients in assessing their problems and needs and in monitoring, planning, and implementing interventions affecting them. As with other development programs, participation is often best fostered by strengthening and drawing on the resources of community and nongovernmental organizations.

Why Should the Government Invest in Early Childhood Development?

Little work has been done on the specific costs and benefits of investing in child development in the Philippines. This section, therefore, begins by reviewing the worldwide evidence on the cost-effectiveness of ECD. It then summarizes the findings of three recent pieces of analytical work on the benefits of preschool education and nutrition in the Philippines. Finally, it reviews the arguments for a governmental role in financing ECD.

General Findings on Cost-Effectiveness

The findings below summarize the experience with ECD investment in general terms. Project-specific summaries of the quantitative results of sixteen ECD projects in developing countries can be found in Section B (taken from Young 1995) of the supplement volume. Other sources that document the cost-effectiveness of investing in ECD are Myers (1992) and World Bank (1992).

HEALTH AND NUTRITION. The kinds of primary care interventions that are typically implemented in ECD programs include prenatal care and education; immunization; oral rehydration therapy; the control of acute respiratory infections; supplementation with vitamin A, iodine, and iron; and growth promotion and supplementary feeding to control PEM. These kinds of interventions are extremely cost-effective. *World Development Report 1993* (World Bank 1993b) ranked the cost-effectiveness of different health care interventions in terms of their cost for each additional year of healthy life they yielded. It concluded that the "EPI Plus" package of interventions, consisting of immunization, and vitamin A and iodine supplementation, ranked among the most cost-effective of all health interventions, costing only $25 to $30 per healthy life-year gained. Growth promotion interventions to control PEM, although more expensive, are nevertheless also cost-effective. The *World Development Report* estimated that food supplementation, for example, is in the middle of the cost-effectiveness range for public health interventions, costing about $63 for each healthy year of life gained, as against $60 to $110 for prenatal and delivery care and $100 to $150 for family planning.

ECD programs focusing on primary care interventions can reduce the number of children who need admission to expensive hospital beds or who require expensive rehabilitation once chronic malnutrition has set in. Primary care interventions thus save money and are efficient. They also have equity benefits. Children of the poor suffer disproportionately from ill health and malnutrition. Giving poor children a better start in life helps reduce disparity by improving their performance in school and their productivity in later life. Nutrition interventions appear to have a particularly strong impact on educational performance. A ten-year study in Mexico demonstrated that severe malnutrition negatively affects school readiness, as does the lack of home stimulation on language development (Chavez and Martinez 1981). Glewwe and Jacoby (1993), in analyzing the Ghana Living Standards Survey, found that nutritional deficiencies in early childhood were associated with delayed primary school enrollment, and argued, based on their survey evidence, that early childhood nutrition interventions can lead to substantial increases in lifetime wealth.

There is striking evidence that nutrition interventions in early childhood prevent death, disability, and degenerative illness, and that they enhance life-long educability and productivity. The lesson from public health nutrition is that poor nutrition in early childhood is a powerful constraint on realizing human potential in poor societies. Operating in synergism with diarrheal, respiratory, and other infections, poor diets in early childhood lead to growth failure, delayed motor and mental development, impaired immunocompetence, and increased risk of complications and death from infections (Waterlow 1992). Child stunting linked with subclinical malnutrition is associated with lowered adult productivity as well as a lasting effect on learning and behavior (Pollitt and others 1993).

Studies in Colombia and Taiwan have shown that food supplementation has a beneficial effect on young children's body size, capacity to work, and cognitive development and performance (Mora and others 1981; McKay and others 1978; Adair and Pollitt 1985). Two well-designed studies, begun in the 1960s in Guatemala and Mexico, clearly demonstrated that poor, rural, breastfed children who received supplementary feeding up to age 2 were taller, had fewer infections, and performed better on appropriate cognitive tests.

Follow-ups of the Guatemala and Mexico studies fifteen years after the intervention confirm the lasting benefits of preventing malnutrition at an early age. In Guatemala several thousand children from the original study were reexamined as adolescents and young adults, and the finding was that supplemented persons had completed more years of schooling and performed better on multifaceted achievement tests compared with children who did not receive the supplement. Moreover, cognitive gains that were small at age 2 were medium to large in the follow-up study (Martorell 1992; Martorell and others 1992). Mexican results were similar (Chavez, Martinez, and Soberanes 1992).

Lastly, the permanent effects of fetal malnutrition on life expectancy and adult health have recently been documented from studies of low birth weights and stunted infants in industrial societies in the early part of the century. Controlled longitudinal studies of British males born in the 1920s and 1930s showed that infants suffering from fetal growth retardation at birth or infants stunted at twelve months had higher mortality as adults from cardiovascular disease, hypertension, and diabetes (Barker 1992).

EARLY EDUCATION. Trying to separate the benefits of early education from those of other ECD interventions is difficult. As in the Mexican study by Chavez and Martinez (1981), where home stimulation was combined with nutrition, early education interventions are usually combined with health and nutrition interventions because of the synergy involved. Even where early education interventions can be separated from other ECD interventions for evaluation purposes, getting a true picture of their benefits is difficult because the most easily quantifiable benefits are in improving school readiness and school performance. Yet early education programs achieve more than school readiness; they also have significant, but hard-to-quantify, longer-term benefits, for example, in terms of improving the socialization of adults. There is therefore both difficulty in measuring the benefits, and some controversy about the magnitude of the benefits, of investing in early education programs alone.

Organized preschool is one common approach to early education for 3- to 6-year-olds. Preschool can have a value beyond the provision of early education alone, if, in an integrated ECD program, the preschool serves as a convergence point for all ECD services. There is clear evidence that, when combined with health and nutrition interventions, well-designed preschool programs can substantially improve the timeliness of school enrollment, reduce the dropout rate of children from school, and increase the performance of children in school. For example, a review by Myers (1992) of nineteen longitudinal evaluations of ECD programs in Latin America showed clear evidence of reduced repetition rates in primary education. And an evaluation of Brazil's PROAPE program showed that this integrated ECD intervention more than paid for itself in reducing the extra cost associated with repeating grades in primary school. The educational benefits of ECD programs are particularly pronounced among traditionally disadvantaged groups, for example, girls and children with rural, indigenous, and lower-level socio-economic backgrounds.

Because ECD programs in developing countries have not been running long or lack monitoring and evaluation systems, it is not possible to determine the long-term effects of these programs on their participants. But a series of evaluations of the Perry Preschool Program and the Head Start Program in the United States have built up considerable evidence of long-term effectiveness. For example, participation in the Perry Program increased the proportion of people who at age 19 were literate (by 60 percent), were enrolled in postsecondary education (by 80 percent), or were employed (by 56 percent), whereas it reduced the percentage who were classified as mentally retarded (by 57 percent), school dropouts (by 35 percent), arrested for criminal activity (by 39 percent), or on welfare (by 43 percent). This program, which began in 1962, was evaluated to have yielded gains of $7 for every dollar invested, in terms of lower education and welfare expenditures and higher productivity among participants (Schweinhart 1993). In 1985 the U.S. Committee for Economic Development concluded that it would be hard to imagine that society could find a higher yield for a dollar of investment than that found in preschool programs for its at-risk children.

Findings for the Philippines

NUTRITION. The international research literature on the nutrition of young children has reached fairly robust quantitative conclusions about the relation between better nutritional status and lower death and disease rates, lower health expenditure, lower mental retardation, higher labor productivity in agriculture, and increased earnings. The PROFILES project, carried out by the Academy for Educational Development with funding from the U.S. Agency for International Development, has developed a computer model that is able to simulate some of these relationships for different levels of and improvements in nutritional status and for different country conditions. The model was first applied in Bangladesh in 1992, and the Asian Development Bank financed the first application of the technology in the Philippines in April 1994. The assumptions underlying the model are based on relationships found in the international literature, modified where appropriate to fit conditions in the Philippines wherever specific research evidence is available. Some details of the PROFILES model and the assumptions made in the Philippines analysis are given in Section C of the supplement volume.

The simulations prepared so far look at six relationships: reduction in PEM, to infant and child deaths; reduction in PEM, to infant and child morbidity; reduction in iodine deficiency, to the number of mentally deficient children born; reduction in anemia, to increased agricultural productivity; reduction in iodine deficiency, malnutrition-induced mortality, and stunting, to total potential wages gained; and reduction in morbidity that is caused by malnutrition-induced acute respiratory infections, diarrhea, and blindness, to government health expenditures.

The simulations show that a nationwide investment in child nutrition would bring very substantial annual benefits. Using 1999 as a basis, the PROFILES model estimates that a 50 percent reduction in PEM would avert more than 37,000 infant and child deaths a year and save more than 150 million days of illness a year. Reducing iodine deficiency by half would prevent more than 15,000 cases of mental retardation every year. The annual benefits of improved nutrition in peso and dollar terms on agricultural productivity, wages gained, and health expenditures are set out in Table 1-1. These benefits are very substantial when set against the likely costs of an effective child nutrition program (estimated in Chapter 5). The calculations are based on projections of the 1990 census population (United Nations 1993a). To accommodate variations in the reliability of the data and the robustness of the assumptions made, a range of benefits is presented for certain nutritional outcomes.

EARLY EDUCATION. Three studies have reviewed the impact of preschool education programs in the Philippines. The first study

Table 1-1. Annual Earnings and Savings from Improvements in Nutrition, Estimates for 1999

	Pesos (millions)	Dollars (millions)
Current earnings from increased agricultural productivity because of a 50 percent reduction in anemia	1,340	48
Future wages gained because of a 50 percent reduction in iodine deficiency, mortality, and stunting	8,400–19,600	300–700
Savings in government health expenditures because of a 50 percent reduction of malnutrition-related diarrhea, blindness, and acute respiratory infections	168–672	6–16

Source: Academy for Education Development (Washington, D.C.) data.

(Child and Youth Research Center 1988) evaluated the impact of the Early Childhood Enrichment Program. As noted in Section B of the supplement volume, this program improved achievement in a range of subjects in the first two grades of elementary school. But this study did not estimate costs, it is not clear whether the improvement had a lasting effect at higher educational grades, and it did not look at alternative ways to improve achievement in primary school, so the relative effectiveness of the program is unclear.

The second study (Mingat and Tan 1995) reviewed the impact of preschool education in general on elementary school outcomes. Of its three significant findings, the first concerned the dropout rate from elementary school: the study concluded that children from poor families are more likely to drop out; that preschool education significantly reduces the likelihood of dropping out (the rate fell from 18 percent to 12 percent for children from poor farming families); and that, from the point of view of dropping out, preschool education fully compensates for the disadvantage of being a poor farmer's child. This study strongly confirms the equity benefits of preschool, which were found in studies in other countries. Again, however, this study did not try to estimate the cost-effectiveness of preschool or compare the impact of preschool to other interventions to reduce the dropout rate from elementary school.

The other main findings of this study related to academic achievement in elementary school. The study found that preschool benefits the children of the better-off more than the children of the poor and that going to preschool for one year affects school performance as much as going for two or more years. These findings seem counterintuitive. They may be an artifact of the study design, which, because of the limitations of the data, was not able to differentiate by the type or quality of preschooling. It is possible that the children of the better-off were able to go to better preschools than the children of the poor and therefore were better prepared for school. Similarly, the finding that a short exposure to preschool is as good as a long one may hold true for preschool as currently organized in the Philippines, but probably does not form a basis for a policy decision about the appropriate length for better-designed, higher-quality preschooling.

The third study (Tan, Land, and Coustere forthcoming) looked at the relative cost-effectiveness of different interventions for increasing student achievement in elementary school. It concluded that preschooling was less effective than providing workbooks or appropriate classroom furniture to elementary students but that it was more cost-effective than reducing class size or increasing teachers' credentials or experience. Because relatively little additional investment is required to provide all elementary students with workbooks and furniture in the Philippines, this study concluded that investing in preschooling was an attractive option.

Each of these studies broadly confirms the experience from other countries that preschooling has significant benefits in equity and school performance. But, because of the way the studies were designed, they provide no guidance as to how long preschool education should be or what preschools should be like to be most cost-effective. More comparative analysis is needed, based on a follow-up of children going to different types of preschools and a look at the costs and effects of different kinds of preschooling.

The Role of Government

HEALTH AND NUTRITION. The fee-for-service private sector provides the curative care the public is prepared to pay for. But without a free public program, there would be little market demand for the preventive care that can obviate the need for much spending on curative care; many people, especially poorer and less-well-educated people, do not perceive the full value of preventive care. The same is true for simple forms of curative care (such as oral rehydration for diarrhea or cotrimoxazole for acute respiratory infections) that can prevent the need for sophisticated and expensive hospital care. Left to the market, many parents will seek medical help for their children too late, when, at worst, a life may be lost and, at best, the cost to the individual and the economy will be higher than it need be. Thus the government's role in paying for a minimum package of public health services on the grounds of market failure is well accepted in the Philippines. As noted above, state intervention to fill the failure of the market in basic health care for young children has very high returns.

There is also a market failure case for public financing of growth promotion interventions to control PEM. Many parents neither realize their children are malnourished nor perceive the effects on growth of small additional amounts of calories. Left to the market, these parents will not intervene. And, left to the market, some very poor parents will be unable to afford the additional food even when they are educated about its benefits. State intervention is justified in principle to demonstrate to all parents the existence of PEM and how to deal with it, and, in the case of a smaller number of food-insecure parents, to provide the wherewithal for them to feed their children properly. The question is not so much whether the state is theoretically justified in intervening as whether the intervention is affordable. For the Philippines, the answer to this question must be yes, because countries such as India, with much lower income levels, are able to spend very substantial resources on national-scale PEM interventions. And indeed, the Philippines already is spending, unproductively, an amount on general food subsidies that would be more than enough to finance an effective child nutrition program (see Chapter 3).

However, questions of the appropriate scale of coverage arise for PEM programs in a way that they do not for programs like immunization, where universal coverage is required to break the chain of disease transmission. PEM affects children progressively less as incomes rise. Geographic targeting is required to ensure that the PEM program is not implemented unnecessarily in better-off areas. A recent survey by the Department of Health identified and mapped the slum populations of two major cities (Metro Manila and Cebu City) on the basis of housing and other environmental conditions; these areas contain about 50 percent of the city population. Thus, one reasonable approach to defining the geographic limits of the PEM program might be to exclude the 50 percent of the urban population who are not slum dwellers.

EARLY EDUCATION. In the Philippines the appropriate role for government in early education is more controversial than in health and nutrition. The key issues center on the role of government in preschool education and day care—areas involving significant capital and recurrent costs—rather than on educational interventions to encourage better parenting. The latter can readily be combined, at minimal additional cost, with health and nutrition outreach services, in which the government's role is clearer. By contrast, preschool and day care centers require dedicated buildings and staff. In principle, government investment in preschool education and day care is justified if it meets three tests: first, the private market is failing to provide services in adequate quantity or quality; second, the intervention is cost-effective; and, third, the intervention is as cost-effective, or more cost-effective, than other interventions the government might make to achieve similar goals.

With regard to the first of the above tests, the data on the extent and quality of private sector preschools are extremely weak. Most accredited private preschools appear to be in urban areas, and the impression from field visits is that rural barangays are very poorly served by the private sector. Until better data can be collected on the distribution of private preschools, it would seem reasonable to assume that the private sector serves no more than the nonslum urban areas, the same areas proposed above for exclusion from the growth promotion program.

With regard to the second and third tests, the only available study on the effectiveness of preschool education in the Philippines is Tan, Land, and Coustere (forthcoming), whose main results were summarized above. Although these studies concluded that pre-schooling reduces the dropout rate from school and improves the performance of those who stay in school, they did not calculate the cost of the current approach to preschool education or look at the costs or the cost-effectiveness of different approaches to pre-schooling. Given the uncertainties about the best way to design a preschool intervention in the Philippines, it can be concluded that not enough is now known for the government to make the very substantial investment required to provide universal preschooling. A good, longitudinal cost-effectiveness study of different ap-proaches to preschooling should be undertaken to determine whether there is a case for this kind of investment.

The study mentioned above did conclude that preschooling in the Philippines is relatively cost-effective in improving educational achievement in elementary school and that preschooling signifi-cantly reduces the school dropout rate among the children of the poor. The study also demonstrated that preschooling has a bigger effect on reducing the dropout rate among the children of poor families than among the children of the better-off. Given these findings and the big disadvantage of the poor in completing school (see Chapter 2), a case might be made for the state to finance preschooling for the poor, provided that the preschooling is ap-propriately designed and preschools are used as convergence points for an integrated set of ECD services, so as to maximize their benefits.

The Philippines already has a rapidly expanding preschool pro-gram, which is set up to benefit about 40 percent of 4- to 6-year-olds in each barangay. (This program is, confusingly, named the Day Care Center Program, although it provides a preschool service rather than daylong child care for working mothers, which is dis-cussed separately below.) Continued government investment in this program appears to be justified provided that its beneficiaries include the children of the poorest families, who do not have the resources to pay for private sector preschooling even if it were available. Even though it is not clear whether this program offers the most cost-effective design or length of preschooling—and more research is needed on this—from an equity perspective, an already mandated program that significantly narrows the differential be-tween poor and rich should not be discontinued until there is hard evidence as to alternatives that are more cost-effective.

Even if continuation of the day care center program is justified, it may still be argued that the duration of the program should be cut from three years to one, based on the Bank's finding that a year of preschool produced no greater impact than two or more years. This finding suggests that, if the Philippines were to invest in universal preschooling, a year of preschool might be adequate for the children of the better-off. But the same conclusion is unlikely to hold for the children of the poor. It is plausible that a longer period of good-quality preschooling may be required to offset the initial disadvantage of these children. It would be unwise to risk penalizing the poor by cutting the current three-year duration of the day care center program until its impact has been properly evaluated. Moreover, such an evaluation should take place only after the quality of the day care center program has been improved, because the Bank study did not control for program quality.

The situation for day care is different because, on the basis of other countries' experience, the role of the private sector is potentially much greater. In addition to providing long-term benefits to society, daylong care offers immediate financial benefits to parents because it frees a parent's time to enter the labor market or to take higher-paying employment outside the home. The experience elsewhere has been that the private sector can meet this demand on a commercial, fee-paying basis. Furthermore, private sector, home-based day care can be quite equitable because low overheads mean that the service is affordable even for poor women, and additional employment for poor women can be generated. Therefore the government should not need to provide widespread daylong care for children of working mothers. If, however, home-based daylong care is not emerging as a result of market forces, as appears to be the situation in the Philippines, there is a case for the government to provide seed money and technical support for demonstration of the viability of home-based day care centers for poor women, as both users and providers of the service.

Conclusions

Government investment in ECD has a high return. The benefits are of several different types, as summarized in Box 1-1. The benefits and the kinds of investment required are clearer for health and nutrition than for early education. But Philippine studies confirm findings in other countries that going to preschool has significant equity effects and is cost-effective in improving performance in elementary school. These studies give little guidance, however, on how early education programs should be designed. Operations research and careful evaluation will be important in this area, but in the meantime, there is a case for strengthening the existing day care center program, provided it remains targeted on the disadvantaged.

2. The Situation of Children in the Philippines

This chapter summarizes the data on the health, nutritional, and psychosocial developmental status of preschool children in the Philippines and discusses what makes children disadvantaged and which children in society are the worst-off. It concludes by outlining the implications for action: ways in which the quality and usefulness of the data for decisionmaking might be improved and what the priorities for intervention programs should be.

Developmental Status

A well-developed preschooler is free of disease, well nourished, and provided with appropriate intellectual, social, and emotional stimulation in a caring environment. This section reviews the developmental status of Filipino preschoolers in each of these dimensions, using quantitative data where available.

Health

CHILD SURVIVAL. The wide range of estimates from different surveys and studies makes it impossible to define the infant and child mortality rates in the Philippines with any certainty. Because of the confusion, in 1991 the government of the Philippines set up a task force on infant mortality. This task force reached a consensus on an infant mortality rate of 57 per 1,000 live births in 1990, the rate now officially adopted. The Philippines has not adopted the under-five mortality rate as an official indicator. One unofficial estimate for this, made by the University of the Philippines Population Institute, is 82 per 1,000 live births in 1990.

Despite some controversy on the exact magnitude of death rates, it is clear that child survival has not improved as far or as fast as it has in other East Asian countries. Thailand and the Philippines had similar infant mortality rates in 1960, for example, but Thailand's rate is now about 30 as against the Philippines' 57 per 1,000 live births. Figure 2-1 illustrates how poorly the reduction in death rates in the Philippines compares with that in other East Asian countries.

DISEASE. The leading diseases among infants and children are respiratory infections and their complications, and diarrhea. But as in other countries, weak data on the incidence and prevalence of disease make it difficult to draw any quantitative conclusions about amounts or trends of disease. According to the Department of Health's statistics, respiratory infection and diarrhea rates among children increased sharply from 1980 to 1990, while at the same time, death rates for the same diseases fell substantially. But the increasing figures for morbidity may say more about greater attention to these diseases and better collection of statistics than about the actual occurrence of these diseases.

Nutrition

MICRONUTRIENT MALNUTRITION. The commonest form of malnutrition in the Philippines is iron deficiency anemia. The reported

Figure 2-1. Percentage Reduction in Death Rates, Selected Countries, 1960–90

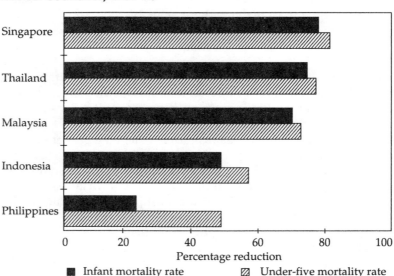

Source: World Bank data.

rates are about 49 percent among infants and about 26 percent among children ages 1 to 6. The high rate among infants reflects the fact that about 43 percent of pregnant and lactating women are anemic. Iron deficiency anemia has important adverse effects on child growth and development, including intellectual performance. The high rates among pregnant women and infants in the Philippines are a serious cause for concern because children's brains develop fastest in the womb and during the first year of life. What is more, recent research has shown that children's development is harmed by even milder levels of anemia than previously thought. WHO is therefore changing the threshold level at which children are defined as anemic, and when the new standard is introduced in the Philippines, an even higher proportion of children will be defined as anemic than is now the case.

There is also an extensive and severe problem of iodine deficiency in the Philippines. The effects of this deficiency include cretinism, mental retardation, reduced learning capacity, and hearing loss in infants and children. Iodine deficiency was traditionally measured as the proportion of the population suffering from goiter; by this measure, iodine deficiency was primarily a regional problem in the Philippines, with six regions of the country having an especially high prevalence. However, recent research has revealed that subclinical levels of iodine deficiency also lead to serious developmental disadvantage in children. A 1993 study of newborns in one Manila hospital revealed that 30 percent of the babies tested suffered from subclinical iodine deficiency. This study is about to be repeated in other urban areas. The findings suggest that iodine deficiency should be considered a national rather than a regional problem.

As with iodine deficiency, vitamin A deficiency was traditionally defined as the proportion of population with clinical signs; by this measure, less than 1 percent of the preschool population in the Philippines is deficient in vitamin A. However, over the past ten years, research has shown that subclinical levels of vitamin A deficiency are highly correlated with increased death rates and that vitamin A supplementation can reduce the child mortality rate by as much as 20 percent. Subclinical vitamin A deficiency is not a problem throughout the Philippines but is widespread in particular populations. For example, a biochemical survey of 1- to 6-year-old children in Davao City in 1992–93 showed 30 percent of children with deficient blood and tissue levels of vitamin A.

PROTEIN-ENERGY MALNUTRITION (PEM). Defining the magnitude of PEM is complicated because the Philippines has adopted a different reference standard for measuring it than the commonly used International Reference Standard for Growth, endorsed by WHO. The differences are important. By the International Reference Standard, about 33 percent of children 0 to 59 months old were underweight (with weight for age less than two standard deviations) in 1992; by the Philippines Reference Standard, only about 11 percent of children were. Using the International Reference Standard, which makes international comparisons possible, PEM in the Philippines was worse in 1992 than in poorer countries such as Egypt, Kenya, Tanzania, and Zimbabwe (United Nations 1993b).

The Philippines Food and Nutrition Research Institute considers the Philippines Reference Standard to be appropriate for the genetic makeup and growth patterns of the Filipino population. However, the International Reference Standard has been advocated because the results of a global study carried out in the 1970s showed that the elites of almost all populations had the same pattern of growth and reached the same height, that is, that genetic influences could be ignored on a population basis and that overall deviations could be attributed to environmental effects. The findings of this study were presented in Eveleth and Tanner (1976), and, on the basis of these and other studies, common reference values were recommended for national use in WHO (1985). If, as seems probable, the international standard is the appropriate one for problem definition, PEM in the Philippines is a major problem.

PEM is a significant national problem in terms of regional equity and trends over time. With regard to the former, PEM rates in 1992 in the two worst-off regions of the country were more than twice what they were in the two best-off regions (Figure 2-2). Also a serious cause for concern and policy action is the slow rate of decline in PEM. During the 1980s, PEM declined more slowly in the Philippines than in not only the better-off countries of East Asia (Malaysia, Thailand) but also the poorer countries of South Asia (Bangladesh, India, Pakistan) (United Nations 1993b). During the 1990s, PEM declined faster, to a level of about 8 percent among 0- to 6-year-old children in 1993. But by the International Reference Standard, this still means that about 29 percent of children are moderately malnourished.

Psychosocial Development

Only one national survey of preschoolers' psychosocial development has been conducted. The survey's usefulness is hampered by the fact that standards for measuring psychosocial development that are specific to conditions in the Philippines have not been

Figure 2-2.   Food Poverty and Protein-Energy Malnutrition (PEM) in the Philippines, by Region, 1991–92

Region

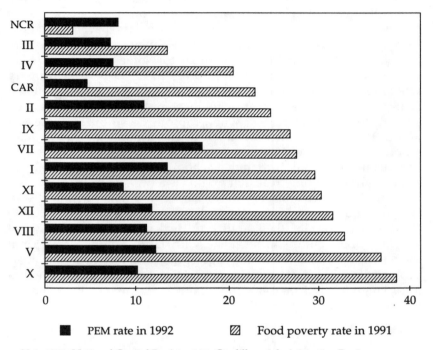

■ PEM rate in 1992   ▨ Food poverty rate in 1991

Note: NCR, National Capital Region; CAR, Cordillera Administrative Region.
Source: For nutrition data, Philippines, FNRI (1992); for food poverty data, final 1991 FIES results.

developed. Indeed, there is no worldwide consensus on the best way to measure this kind of development. Limited evidence makes it difficult to draw firm conclusions about the seriousness of the problem and hence about the importance of investing in early education.

The national survey referred to above was a 1986 study of 0- to 6-year-olds carried out by the Child and Youth Research Center (1988). The study assessed psychosocial development by measuring the child's conformity with normative definitions of developmental stages in eating, elimination, grooming, dressing, coping, and play at different ages. Twenty marginal communities were sampled, including urban poor, offshore island, fishing, tribal, and plantation worker communities, and communities with high levels of seasonal unemployment. The study found that most children's performance was within the norm, although about 10 percent of children showed delays in language development and 5 percent showed delays in cognitive development. If this study is valid, the relatively low levels of disadvantage in marginal communities suggest still lower levels in the broader population.

However, indirect evidence about preschoolers' psychosocial development, based on how they do in elementary school, is more worrying. Test results are lower than for some other East Asian countries, and, although the Philippines has a 99 percent primary school enrollment rate, dropout rates are unacceptably high. Only 68 percent of grade 1 entrants actually complete elementary school; 60 percent of the 32 percent who drop out do so during grades 1 and 2. It is not known how much of the dropout is due to poor school readiness and how much to other factors, such as poverty, distance from school, inadequate school facilities and materials, or poor-quality teaching; research on this is a high priority. However, high dropout rates and poor performance in school must partly be the consequence of inadequate school readiness among Filipino children in terms of their ability to deal with different ways of learning, their ability to socialize with large groups of children their own age, and their language skills. The last is a particular problem for preschoolers who have been brought up to speak a local language and then have to adapt to teaching in both the national language and English in primary school.

Causes of Disadvantage

What are the causes of death and disease, malnutrition, and poor psychosocial development? Because of the lack of data on psychosocial development, most of the following discussion, as well as nearly all of the quantitative analysis, focuses on disease and malnutrition.

Disease

ECONOMIC DEVELOPMENT AND DISEASE. Trends in infant and child health indicators during the past thirty years have been closely related to economic development and social sector spending. This can best be seen through changes in the infant mortality rate, because the morbidity data are not reliable enough for trend analysis. The infant mortality rate fell rapidly during the 1960s, when the Philippines was prospering, but the decline stalled in the late 1970s and throughout the 1980s. This stall paralleled a period during the Marcos government when economic growth stagnated and there was underinvestment in child survival interventions. Investment was also very limited in social development programs that indirectly but strongly affect child health, such as water and sanitation, nutrition, and family planning.

During the Aquino and Ramos governments, there was increased investment in a range of public health services, including immunization and the control of diarrhea, acute respiratory infections, malaria, tuberculosis, and schistosomiasis (see Chapter 5). By 1990 the performance of the immunization and diarrheal disease control programs had improved substantially (see Chapter 3). These programs and other recent interventions should lead to a continuing fall in the infant mortality rate when the results of the next survey are available. The initial impact of additional public health investment, together with the ending of the recession of the mid-1980s, may explain the drop in the national infant mortality rate from 63 per 1,000 lives in 1986 to 57 per 1,000 live births in 1990 (Figure 2-3). The overall progress in health during that period should be interpreted with caution, however, because the infant mortality

Figure 2-3. Infant Mortality Rate in Selected Regions of the Philippines, Selected Years, 1976–90

Deaths per 1,000 live births

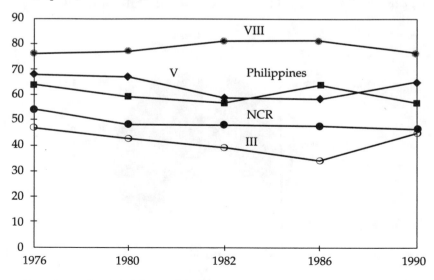

Note: NCR is the National Capital Region.
Source: National demographic surveys of the Philippines.

Figure 2-4. Causes of Infant Deaths in the Philippines, 1990

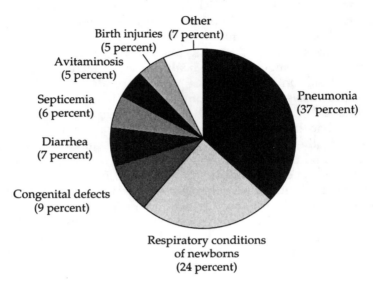

Note: "Other" includes measles (3 percent), meningitis (2 percent), and bronchitis (2 percent).
Source: Philippines, Department of Health data.

Figure 2-5. Causes of Infant Morbidity in the Philippines, 1990

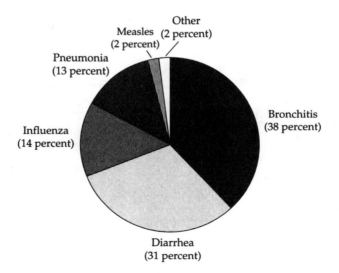

Source: Philippines, Department of Health data.

rate actually increased in eight of the country's thirteen regions
from 1986 to 1990. Figure 2-3 takes data from four regions to illus-
trate the variance in trends. It also shows the continuing extreme
variance in the levels of infant mortality rate between regions, with
infant mortality rates in the more backward regions, such as Eastern Visayas and parts of Mindanao, more than 50 percent higher
than those in the better-off parts of the country. Section D in the
supplement volume shows the 1990 infant mortality rates for each
of the regions.

THE PROXIMATE CAUSES OF DEATH AND DISEASE. The relative importance of different diseases in 1990 is summarized in Figures 2-4
to 2-7. The charts demonstrate the overwhelming importance of
pneumonia as a cause of death for both infants and children. The
importance of diarrhea-related dehydration as a cause of death
varies significantly by region; in provinces such as Samar, where
sanitation and water supply are poor, it can account for as much as
half of child deaths. The pattern of morbidity is similar. Among
both infants and children, bronchitis and influenza—both of which
can lead to pneumonia—make up more than half of reported morbidity. Diarrhea is the next most important disease. Malaria, although not a major child health problem at the national level, is a
leading cause of morbidity in areas where it is endemic, and it is
probably underreported, being often recorded simply as fever.

As in other countries, the cause-of-death data oversimplify what
is actually happening. Most infant and child deaths are the result
of a combination of causes, only one of which is usually recorded.
The risk of death rises in a nonlinear way with the number of risks
a child faces. For example, a child suffering from malnutrition,
diarrhea, and a respiratory infection has much more than three
times the risk of dying than a child suffering from only one of
these potential causes of death. PEM, which is unrecorded, is the
greatest hidden cause of death. This multiple causation of death
has important implications for the design of intervention programs—limiting the effectiveness of programs to control a single
disease and giving a correspondingly high payoff to an integrated
approach to attacking disease and malnutrition.

Attacking disease among infants remains the priority, because
more than two-thirds of the deaths of preschoolers occur among
infants. Of these infant deaths, 46 percent occur within the first
month of life, and 35 percent within the first week, indicating the
key importance of educating mothers and providing antenatal care
during pregnancy and of providing services during the neonatal
period. As for children, progress toward universal immunization

**Figure 2-6.   Causes of Deaths of Children Ages 1 to 4
in the Philippines, 1990**

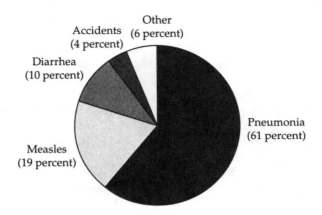

Note: "Other" includes bronchitis (2 percent), heart disease (2 percent), and other diseases (2 percent).
Source: Philippines, Department of Health data.

**Figure 2-7.   Causes of Morbidity in Children Ages 1 to 4
in the Philippines, 1990**

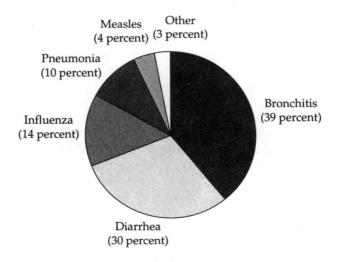

Source: Philippines, Department of Health data.

may well have reduced the incidence of measles significantly since 1990, leaving pneumonia and diarrhea as the main causes of death.

CONTRIBUTORY CAUSES OF DEATH AND DISEASE. Countries that have rapidly improved child health have invested not only in direct interventions such as immunization and oral rehydration therapy, but also in programs that indirectly affect child deaths and disease. Although these include all programs aimed at combating poverty and inequity, those that have the greatest impact on health status are programs in the areas of water and sanitation, maternal health, family planning, and nutrition. Programs for female education have also been important, but pay off only in the long term.

Substantial improvements have been made in the coverage of both safe-water and sanitation programs: in Section E of the supplement volume, Figures 1 and 2, taken from World Bank (1993a), show coverage differences by region between 1980 and 1990 for both programs. In most regions, more than two-thirds of families now have adequate sanitation, and more than three-quarters have access to safe water. But the same tables also show continuing regional differences, which are more marked for safe water than for sanitation. Lagging regions for access to safe water are II, IX, and XII, and for sanitation coverage, XI and XII.

Performance has been much less satisfactory in maternal health care programs, and especially in family planning, which is a key health intervention for both mothers and children. The total fertility rate in the Philippines is 4.1 and the modern-method contraceptive prevalence rate a low 25 percent. Frequent, closely spaced births lead to a gradual depletion of the mother's health and nutritional status and the mother's capacity to nourish children in the womb and care for them once born. The costs in terms of child mortality of failing to plan families are well established. For the Philippines, it has been estimated (World Bank 1991) that both the infant and child mortality rates would decline by as much as 25 percent if pregnancy were avoided by women younger than twenty and older than forty-five, women who have four or more children, and women who are within fifteen months of their last birth. Underinvestment in and weak commitment to family planning in the years prior to the Ramos government have taken a heavy toll of children's, as well as women's, lives.

The links between severe malnutrition and high rates of infant mortality and morbidity have long been recognized. Through depressing the immune system, PEM makes children more liable to catch infections and slower to recover from them; severe PEM can increase the risk of death by up to eight times. Only more recently

Figure 2-8. Percentage of Child Deaths Caused by a Combination of Infection and Protein-Energy Malnutrition (PEM), Selected Countries

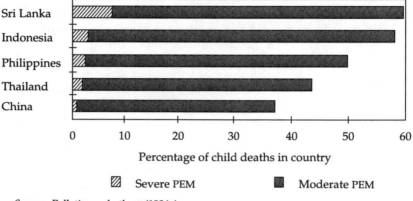

Percentage of child deaths in country

☑ Severe PEM   ■ Moderate PEM

Source: Pelletier and others (1994a).

has research demonstrated that the risks are not limited to severe PEM but form a gradually declining continuum through severe and moderate PEM. Pelletier and others (1994a) have estimated contributory effects of PEM for fifty-three developing countries. Figure 2-8 presents their data, for a sample of Asian countries, on the proportion of child deaths that are the combined result of infection and PEM. "Moderate" malnutrition is associated with nearly half of child deaths in the Philippines, indicating that gains from further investment in child health programs may be limited unless accompanied by equally determined efforts to improve nutrition.

Malnutrition

In every country, the nutritional status of children depends on their food security, their health, and the quality of the care they receive. Disentangling which of these factors are important causes of malnutrition is essential if governments are to choose the most cost-effective balance of investment between programs to combat poverty and food insecurity; health programs; and programs to change behavior. The following sections discuss the causes of PEM at some length because these are not universally understood.

PEM, POVERTY, AND FOOD INSECURITY. Many legislators and government officials in the Philippines assume, understandably, that malnutrition is simply the result of poverty and lack of purchasing power for food. This view is encouraged by the correlation that can be seen at the broadest level between trends in economic growth and trends in malnutrition. Figure 2-9 shows the trends in the gross domestic product (GDP) index against the trends in wasting and stunting. It illustrates how rapidly falling malnutrition correlated with steady economic growth until 1982 and then how nutritional improvement slowed and, in the case of wasting, began to deteriorate during the period of economic crisis and slow growth between 1983 and 1992. Recently available survey data for 1993 show a continuation in the trend of improvement in stunting and deterioration in wasting. But a review of other data shows that the relationship between poverty and malnutrition is more complicated than the broad national trends suggest.

Two main definitions of poverty are used in the Philippines. The poverty line is the threshold below which people have insufficient income to pay for minimum food and nonfood needs. The subsistence poverty, or food poverty, line is the threshold below which

Figure 2-9. Trends in Economic Growth and in Wasting and Stunting of Children Age 5 and Under, Philippines, 1978–92

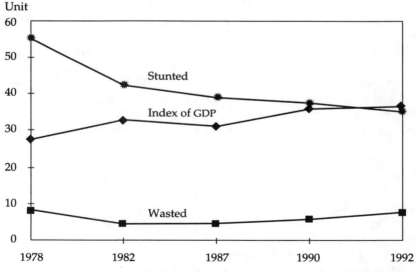

Note: Wasting is low weight for height, an indicator of current malnutrition. Stunting is low height for age, an indicator of cumulative malnutrition over time.

Source: For nutrition data, Philippines, FNRI surveys; for GDP index, derived from data in World Bank (1993a).

people have insufficient income to buy even their minimum requirements of food. The food poverty index is a more appropriate measure for nutrition comparisons than the poverty index is. The government estimated that about 20 percent of the population was below the food poverty threshold in 1991. The levels at which both thresholds have been set have been criticized on methodological grounds (World Bank 1993a); both may overestimate the amount of poverty. But for this analysis, the levels of these indicators are less significant than their trends and their distribution across regions.

Food poverty fell from 24 percent of the population in 1985 to 20 percent in 1988 and remained at about the 1988 level in 1991, according to the government statistics. These national trends hide great interregional variation. Between 1988 and 1991, food poverty fell quite sharply in the National Capital Region (NCR) and Regions VI, VII, and VIII (most of the Visayas), whereas it rose in Regions II, III, X, XI, and XII. What is of interest is to see how far changes in malnutrition match these changes in food poverty. Between 1988 and 1991, malnutrition fell in Regions III, VIII, and IX; food poverty did not fall in any of these regions. PEM increased significantly in ten regions; food poverty increased significantly in only five. PEM and food poverty moved in completely opposite directions in four regions: in the NCR and Regions VI and VII, PEM rose while poverty declined, and in Region III nutritional status improved while poverty worsened. Thus, when looking beyond the broad, national aggregates, rising and falling poverty levels seem to have no clear correlation with movements in PEM.

Figure 2-2 shows the food poverty rate for 1991 and the prevalence of underweight preschoolers for 1992 by region. (Comparing survey data for poverty and for PEM is difficult because they are seldom available for the same year. But although the comparison in Figure 2-2 is not exact, neither is it likely to be invalid, because these indicators do not change very substantially in a single year.) Clearly, for regional distribution as well as for trends over time, the relationship between PEM and food poverty is not close. The relatively low levels of malnutrition in the very poor Regions V, IX, and X and the high levels of malnutrition in the better-off Regions III and the NCR stand out in particular as apparent anomalies. The same pattern, or lack of it, holds if PEM rates are compared with poverty rates as opposed to food poverty rates.

Overall, therefore, the imperfect correlation between poverty, food security, and PEM suggests that other important causative factors are at work. The following sections look at the importance of health and care, as well as food security, in determining the nutritional status of preschoolers of different ages.

LOW BIRTH WEIGHT. About 15 percent of newborn babies weigh less than the norm of 2.5 kg (the reported figure is 18 percent, but this may be an overestimate). For these children, PEM begins in the womb because their mothers' nutritional status during pregnancy is inadequate to give the fetus the nutrients it needs to develop fully. Maternal nutrition is therefore a major determinant of child nutrition in the Philippines. Unfortunately, there are no data from large samples on the nutritional status of pregnant women. However, data from the 1993 Safe Motherhood Survey (Philippines, National Statistics Office 1994) provide the first national-level assessment of the PEM status of women of reproductive age in general. They show that more than 12 percent of women have a body mass index (a combined measure of weight and height) less than 18.5, the level indicating chronic undernutrition and likely adverse effects on fetal growth for those who are pregnant. A low body mass index affects more than 15 percent of women who live in rural areas, of women who have no more than primary education, and of women less than 20 years old. These are the women who, when faced with the additional biological demands of pregnancy, are likely to have babies with low birth weights.

The causes of poor maternal nutrition before pregnancy are unclear. Although there is evidence that intrahousehold allocation of food discriminates against women (Senauer, Garcia, and Jacinto 1988), the same study showed that the difference between men's caloric intake and women's was much less than the difference between the intakes of both men and women and the recommended daily allowance. Food insecurity is likely to explain a larger proportion of prepregnancy nutritional deficits than cultural and behavioral factors. Undereating because of food insecurity is almost certainly compounded during pregnancy by failure to adequately increase food intake, either through ignorance of the additional food-energy demands of pregnancy or for other reasons, such as fear of having a large baby and a difficult delivery. The limited evidence on this score is disturbing; the pregnant women from three poor provinces who were monitored in the Senauer study increased their caloric intake by less than a third of the addition required for adequate weight gain.

Additional food intake is also required during lactation to meet the demands of producing breast milk. An important study of lactation in Cebu (Adair and Popkin 1992) showed that, for a high proportion of women, maternal weight loss after pregnancy cumulated through subsequent births in a cycle of maternal depletion. The study showed that, for poor rural women, energy intakes

during lactation were low, at about half of recommended allowances. Of such women, no less than 28 percent started the next
pregnancy with a body mass index lower than 18.5. In addition to
the need for supplementary feeding for such at-risk pregnant
women, these data indicate that family planning is important for
nutrition, because better spacing of births allows more time for
women to recover weight.

Finally, in addition to the short-term effect on low birth weight
of how well women are nourished during their reproductive period, there is also a long-term intergenerational effect of malnutrition among women. Baby girls with low birth weights are likely to
grow into small women, who in turn are more likely than average
to have small babies—a vicious cycle that can be broken only with
improved nutrition over a generation.

PEM AND FEEDING PRACTICES. It is unclear whether food insecurity, as expressed through maternal deficits during lactation, reduces the availability of breast milk to the child. Much more
clear—from a detailed study of breastfeeding patterns in Cebu (Zohoori, Popkin, and Fernandez 1991)—is that the breastfeeding behavior of a high proportion of mothers is inimical to the healthy
growth of the child. This study showed that by the age of 2 months
only 27 percent of infants were exclusively breastfed, with about 20
percent being fed nonnutritious liquids in addition to breast milk
and about 38 percent getting other nutritious liquids as well. Aside
from the fact that other liquids are likely to be less nutritious than
breast milk, research (Popkin and others 1990) has shown that,
given the poor hygiene practices commonly prevailing in developing countries, feeding additional foods or liquids at this age can
double or triple the likelihood of diarrhea, thus further threatening
nutritional status.

The Cebu data are reinforced by national estimates derived from
the 1993 National Demographic Survey (Philippines, National Statistics Office 1994). Breastfeeding of children is less common in the
Philippines than in many developing countries. Among infants
younger than 3 months, only a third are exclusively breastfed, and
about 17 percent are not breastfed at all. The remaining half are
given water, other liquids, or soft foods in addition to breast milk.
Weaning comes at an early age according to the survey. Between 4
and 6 months, the proportion of infants who are exclusively breastfed drops to less than 10 percent, and fewer than 2 percent of children older than 6 months are exclusively breastfed. The links to
infection through contaminated food or drink are also suggested
by the fact that the highest incidence of diarrhea occurs among

weaned children 6 to 11 months old (17 percent), followed by children 12 to 23 months old (15.6 percent).

Complementary feeding becomes increasingly important after the age of 6 months because the child's caloric requirements increase and can no longer be fully met by breast milk. Inadequate feeding of solid foods can be due either to a late start to weaning or to the inadequacy of the amounts fed. Both the Cebu study and the 1992 National Nutrition Survey indicate that, in the Philippines, weaning begins on time. The feeding problem appears to be related either to the amount fed (the child is not fed to satiation) or to the fact that traditional weaning foods are not dense enough in calories to nourish the child adequately, even though it is no longer hungry. Because of the very small amounts of additional food required at this age, it is probable that the rise in PEM before the age of 2 is the result of these kinds of poor feeding practices, rather than food insecurity. And it is probable that most mothers feed too little because they do not realize their children are malnourished. Moderate PEM, the predominant form of PEM in the Philippines, is not easily recognizable to the untrained eye.

The increase in PEM at this point is also due to the increased prevalence of infections in the second year; both of the most prevalent infections—diarrhea and acute respiratory infections—lead to weight loss. Increased exposure to infection arises from both greater mobility and increasing dependence on a frequently contaminated food supply. This takes place in conjunction with declining intakes of breast milk and its constituent maternal antibodies. Data from Cebu (Zohoori, Popkin, and Fernandez 1991) indicate that about 22 percent of rural mothers and 46 percent of urban mothers have stopped breastfeeding by the time the child is 12 months old. Low resistance to disease is also caused by the delays in the development of immunocompetence associated with malnutrition.

From the age of 2 onward wasting falls sharply (Figure 2-10). This pattern, seen in many developing countries, usually reflects the child's growing immunity to infection, coupled with an increasing intake of solid foods as the child is able to eat for itself rather than rely only on what it is fed by the mother. In the Philippines, the drop in wasting is from 15 percent to only about 5 percent of children. From this point on, PEM is less likely to be related to behavior and more likely to be related to food insecurity, because the child's food needs have increased and may be beyond the purchasing power of the poorest families. (Food insecurity likely is also the main cause of the high prevalence of wasting among 7- to 10-year-old school-age children, which was a very worrying finding of the 1992 survey by the Food and Nutrition Research Institute.)

Figure 2-10.   Age-Specific Wasting and Stunting in the Philippines, 1992

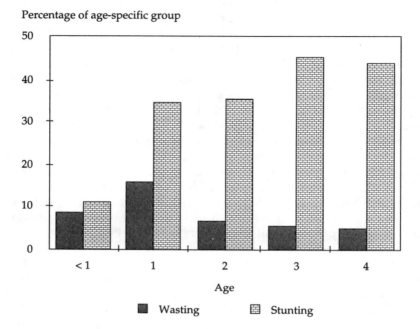

Percentage of age-specific group

Source: Philippines, FNRI National Nutrition Survey.

The sharp decline in wasting after the age of 2 indicates that most families with a nutrition problem can afford to feed their children even when their children's intakes are increasing and they are becoming more expensive to feed. This has important implications for policy: most of the PEM seen in preschoolers appears to be stunting caused by the legacy of poor feeding practices and poor health at the time of weaning, rather than being caused by food insecurity.

Although it is not possible to derive from the above analysis any quantitative conclusions about the relative importance of food, health, and care in determining PEM in the Philippines, it is clear that, especially for children under 3, disease and poor feeding practices play a very important role. The conclusion for policy is that, although food insecurity is one important cause of malnutrition in the Philippines, efforts to improve food security alone will not suffice to control malnutrition. They will need to be accompanied by equally determined efforts to improve health services (including family planning) and the health and nutritional behavioral practices of caregivers.

MICRONUTRIENT MALNUTRITION. Micronutrient malnutrition is mainly the result of the unbalanced diets of Filipino women and children, although parasites and geological conditions are also a factor. As with PEM, poor weaning practices—more specifically, an inadequate balance of nutrients in weaning foods—are a major factor. The dietary iron intakes of pregnant and lactating women were reported by the National Nutrition Survey to be only 62 percent and 55 percent, respectively, of recommended levels in 1987. Furthermore, this iron is derived mostly from vegetables and hence is poorly absorbed. Although vitamin C enhances iron absorption from vegetables, per capita consumption of fruit and vegetables containing vitamin C has been declining in the Philippines. In addition to diet, parasites—malarial, schistosomal, and helminthic—cause iron loss in ecological zones where these are prevalent. Low uptake of iron from the diet, combined with accelerated loss from reproduction and parasitic disease, rapidly depletes maternal iron stores. Inadequate iron stores are then established in the fetus, and iron deficiency anemia emerges in infancy.

Vitamin A deficiency results from low dietary intake of retinol and carotene from meat and green and yellow vegetables. It is primarily a consequence of the cereal-based diet in the Philippines. Breast milk is an important source of vitamin A in early childhood, and low maternal stores result in the early onset of xeropthalmia in childhood. The deficiency in children is also exacerbated by infections, particularly measles and its complications.

Geological conditions explain low levels of iodine in the food chain. Although there is no evidence that naturally occurring food goitrogens have a role in this condition, high levels of cassava intake may be a problem in some areas. In endemic areas, iodine derived from the diet is inadequate to meet normal demands for women's health and is exacerbated by the additional requirements of reproduction. As with iron, the deficiency is passed on to the fetus and subsequently to the infant.

Inadequate Psychosocial Development

Persistent poor health and malnutrition are themselves important causes of inadequate psychosocial development. They can inhibit the development of intelligence and of neurological and psychomotor systems. Also, children who are ill or have PEM are less active; consequently, they play less, they respond less well to stimulation, they are less sociable, and they are less attentive to their environment and learn less from it. Other important influences on psychosocial development include the degree to which children receive loving attention and stimulation from caregivers (this has both a time and a quality dimension), the amount and quality of interaction they have with other children, and the richness of their environment in terms of the things they have to play with or learn from. In general, the types of families who are least likely to be able to provide for the adequate psychosocial development of their children are the very poor and the children of poor, formal sector employees in urban areas.

The very poor have to work hardest to make ends meet. Both parents work long hours, when they can find work. Time spent with young children may be limited, especially at seasons of peak agricultural employment. Quality time with children may be still more limited because very poor parents are themselves more likely to be ill, malnourished, or tired, and so have less energy for childcare. The very poor are also least likely to be able to provide an appropriate environment for their children; they may have no protected water supply and may live in unsanitary surroundings. And the very poor are least likely to be able to pay for childcare while they work.

There is little hard data for the Philippines on the quantity and quality of childcare among the poor. However, the Cebu breast-feeding study (Zohoori, Popkin, and Fernandez 1991) found a clear seasonal pattern in the time spent on breastfeeding, with a thirty-three-minute difference in the daily time devoted to this activity between peak and trough, suggesting that agricultural work significantly affects caring practices. One study of women's work and infant care in Cebu (Doan and Popkin 1992) showed that nearly 60 percent of mothers work outside the home, many of them in occupations that preclude taking their children with them. Grandmothers become the primary caregivers to children in these cases. The same study showed that poor women with several preschoolers were the mothers most likely to be working outside the home. Thus, economic necessity appears to impel into the labor market the poorest women, who may be in the weakest position to arrange adequate care for their children.

Among the poor, those living in urban areas are likely to have the greatest difficulty in providing adequately for the psychosocial development of their children, because a high (but unknown) proportion of them are migrants to the city who have left behind them in the province the extended family network that provided childcare services. Children who in the village might have been left in the care of a grandmother, or someone else experienced in parenting, may in the urban slum be left in the care of a sibling. This type of childcare problem extends also to many better-off parents who are working in factories but not earning enough to pay for organized day care. Because more than 37 percent of women participate in the work force in the Philippines, and rural-urban migration rates remain high, this type of potential disadvantage is large and growing.

The Worst-off

The Ramos government was elected with a special mandate to improve equity and empower the poor. This section summarizes what is known about who and where the most disadvantaged children are.

What Are the Risk Factors?

Depending on where they live and what kind of family they come from, children are subject to different types, levels, and combinations of developmental risk. At least six main types of risk factors can be identified, as follows:

- *Demographic.* As noted above, infants are more at risk than children, and neonates are the most at-risk infants. Closely spaced children and children with many siblings are less likely to get adequate care, as are the children of single parents.
- *Income-related.* Income is heavily dependent on educational level and occupation. Particularly low-earning occupations in the Philippines include those of part-time informal sector workers in urban areas; traditional fishermen; and landless laborers, who in addition to low wages suffer from seasonal employment fluctuations and the energy demands of hard physical work.
- *Environmental.* Children who live in environments which encourage malaria, schistosomiasis, and helminths are at particular risk, as are children who live where there is no protected water supply or adequate sanitation.
- *Geographic.* Remoteness is also a risk factor. Children living on smaller offshore islands, in coastal communities only reachable by water, and in mountain and forest areas, are hardest to reach with outreach services and are hard to get to referral facilities.

- *Peace and order.* Armed conflict reportedly led to the displacement of 1.36 million people since 1986 (HEWSPECS 1994). Although since 1991 there has been a sharp decline in insurgency-related violence, many of the areas previously affected still suffer from a legacy of inaccessibility and under-provision of services.
- *Cultural.* An estimated 1.0 million to 1.5 million preschoolers (10 to 15 percent of the preschool-age population) are children of indigenous communities, which can be defined as groups with a social or cultural identity distinct from the dominant society, and this makes them vulnerable to being disadvantaged in the development process. Section F in the supplement volume summarizes the main population groups involved. The government wishes to give special priority to child development among these peoples.

Although any one of the above risk factors may be enough to cause disadvantage, the worst-off families are usually affected by a combination of risk factors. Indigenous communities, for example, are often very poor, live in remote areas, and live in areas that are or were areas of armed conflict. Slum and street children are the children of the very poor, live in extremely unhealthy environments, are dependent on street foods for their nutrition, and have few opportunities for stimulation and play.

Where Are the Worst-off?

Regions that have both high levels of infant mortality and high PEM rates among preschoolers are likely to be among the most disadvantaged from a child development perspective. Figure 2-2 and Section D in the supplement volume indicate that the regions falling in this category are V, VI, and VIII—Bicol and Eastern and Western Visayas. In addition, Regions II, IX, and the CAR have high infant mortality rate levels but lower PEM rates, and Regions I and VII have high PEM rates but lower infant mortality rates. If food poverty is included as an indicator, Regions X, XI, and XII also join the list, but none of them have very high infant mortality rates or PEM rates. Regions III, IV, and the NCR are the best-off, with low rates for all three indicators.

However, comparing rates of disadvantage between regions gives an inaccurate picture when the magnitude of the problem is defined in numbers of disadvantaged children. For example, the six worst regions as measured by PEM rates were, in order, VII, VI, I, V, IX, and VIII in 1992. But as measured in numbers of malnourished preschoolers, the order is VI, VII, IV, V, the NCR, and I. Although Region IV and the NCR do not even figure in the top six for PEM rates, they are very important in relation to numbers. Between them, in 1992, they contained more than 19 percent of the malnourished preschoolers in the Philippines.

Below the regional level, it becomes difficult to define child disadvantage, because there are no reliable data for either infant mortality rate or PEM rates at the provincial or municipal level. The government has ranked provinces in terms of disadvantage using a weighted indicator that includes measures of illiteracy, infant mortality, malnutrition, sanitation, and the head count and poverty gap definitions of poverty. For different program purposes, twenty-five and nineteen priority provinces have been defined. There is some argument about the appropriateness of the methodology for this ranking (see World Bank 1993a and Balisacan 1993), both because the data for several of the constituent indicators are weak and because the weightings used are debatable. But what is perhaps most important is that simple targeting by province leaves extremely disadvantaged children in other provinces out of the count, and their numbers may be substantial. For example, neither the nineteen nor the twenty-five priority areas include the NCR, with its very large numbers of disadvantaged slum children.

There are, therefore, several problems in defining who and where the worst-off are. First, the statistics currently collected are designed each to measure just one aspect of risk, but they are not aggregated to measure the combinations of risk that define the most disadvantaged. Second, the geographic areas, such as slums, in which the most disadvantaged live do not correspond to the geographic units, based on administrative structures, for which statistics are collected. Third, although we know which types of families are likely to be worst-off and which broad geographic areas they are most likely to be found in, the aggregated data available do not permit identification of the families most in need.

Implications for Action

The type, quality, and availability of data determine how good a judgment can be made about what interventions to make and also how well interventions can be targeted to client groups. What might be done to make the data on children more useful? What are the most important intervention programs to improve child development?

Data for Determining Interventions

RISK PROFILES. As stated earlier, intervening to tackle only one source of disadvantage will do little to improve the overall status of children suffering from combinations of risk. Collecting data on the risk profiles of different types of disadvantaged groups is an important first step in determining the set of program interventions that will best respond to their needs. The Department of Health is beginning an innovative project to try to determine the overall health risks affecting slum dwellers in the Philippines, using geographic information systems to overlay data on risks of different types to give a total risk profile. Interventions will then be adapted to respond. This project will provide risk profiles for one set of disadvantaged children. It would be useful to extend this approach to prepare risk profiles of other important disadvantaged child groups, such as children of indigenous peoples and small-scale plantation workers.

IRON DEFICIENCY. As indicated, there is some uncertainty over the levels of iron deficiency in infants. Intervening to reduce anemia in infants is much more expensive than it is for older children because infants can take iron only in liquid form, at the cost of P35 ($1.23) for each child treated, rather than the much cheaper tablet form. Because routine supplementation of all infants may not be cost-effective, improving the data on infant iron deficiency would help to assist in deciding who should get supplementation.

PEM. Although the existing nutrition survey data give a good picture of infant and child PEM, anthropometric data on PEM in pregnant and lactating women are lacking, as indicated earlier. A survey to provide these data would help in defining strategies for improving women's health and nutritional status and reducing low birth weight. Better data on low birth weight would also be useful, both because the current data are for hospital births, and hence may not be representative of the total population, and because the current data do not distinguish between prematurity and intrauterine growth retardation as causes of low birth weight. For all types of PEM, there is a great need for better qualitative data on the beliefs and behaviors that lead to inadequate or improper feeding.

PSYCHOSOCIAL DEVELOPMENT. The almost complete absence of data on the psychosocial development of children makes it difficult to decide what priority should be given to investment in this area or what the needs of specific groups are. Before carrying out surveys in this area, it should be determined whether the indicators that have been used to measure psychosocial development in the Philippines are the most appropriate. Doing so would involve taking the developmental standards for preschoolers that have been used in the Philippines and other countries and adapting them to social and cultural conditions, both nationally and for specific cultural groups within the country. This would be a complex task for specialists in sociology, education, and developmental psychology. Once this first step has been taken, the priority would be to carry out a survey of the developmental status of children as they enter school. Data collected at this point in a child's life are useful for reorienting both ECD interventions and school teaching methods and content to make them appropriate for the needs of incoming children.

Data for Targeting and Monitoring

Although the main causes of disease and the related interventions are well understood, the data for targeting risk groups and monitoring progress in disease reduction remain weak.

MORBIDITY AND MALNUTRITION. As indicated, it is notoriously difficult to collect accurate morbidity data through statistics on services. Yet targeting and monitoring morbidity will become more important as attention shifts to child development as well as child survival. Developing an effective disease surveillance system at and below the provincial level will therefore be important. With this in mind, the Department of Health has been developing a streamlined set of health indicators for making rapid assessments, and these indicators will be piloted in two regions before being used nationally. By 2000, the plan is for each region to have an epidemiology unit capable of training and supporting provincial staff in applied epidemiology and cluster surveys. The plan also calls for trained personnel in the twenty-five priority provinces to disseminate public health information to local government officials for use in planning and monitoring.

Getting good data on the extent of micronutrient deficiency is also impossible from statistics on services, because field staff cannot detect subclinical (but harmful) levels of deficiency during routine contacts with patients; blood or tissue analysis is required. This is another area where development of a sentinel surveillance system for measuring levels and trends and targeting disadvantaged groups will be important.

THE MOST DISADVANTAGED. Mapping the geographic areas where the most disadvantaged are, as the Department of Health is doing in the case of slum dwellers, is a satisfactory targeting mechanism where the worst-off are concentrated together. But although some of the worst-off live together (for example, slum dwellers and some indigenous peoples), most disadvantaged children live scattered among families who are better-off. Targeting these disadvantaged children raises issues of design and cost-effectiveness, because the most accurate targeting systems are also the most difficult to manage and the most expensive.

At least three different mechanisms are currently used or planned to target services to at-risk families and individuals within communities. First, the Department of Social Welfare and Development uses a family survey questionnaire that attempts to measure economic self-sufficiency, social adequacy, sociocultural factors, family functioning, and role performance. Second, in the provinces targeted by the government's and UNICEF's Area-Based Child Survival and Development Program, field personnel screen for at-risk families, defined as those with a moderately or severely malnourished preschooler and at least one of the following characteristics: a mother or father with chronic illness, an illiterate mother, a working mother, and unemployed or underemployed parents. Under the same project, high-risk families were defined as those with at least three of these characteristics. Third, the Department of Health now plans to begin using a "life-cycle" mechanism, in which services will be focused on those in the most vulnerable stages of life, notably pregnant and lactating women and preschool children (see Section G in the supplement volume for details).

Although all the above mechanisms have merit, it is also clear that the complexity of targeting systems is increasing, calling into question how often communities can cost-effectively be surveyed and how consistently and with what quality targeting decisions will be made. These questions are a special concern in the more uncertain environment since the responsibility for implementing health and family welfare services devolved.

One priority for dialogue between the social sector agencies would therefore be the development of a "quick and clean" set of indicators for identifying the most disadvantaged in each community and ensuring that they get access to the full range of services to which they are entitled. For children, such a system might be based on first defining the target group of pregnant and lactating women and preschoolers by implementing the life-cycle mechanism and then identifying families actually or potentially at risk within this group by measuring family assets and PEM status as proxies for the whole range of indicators of disadvantage. Family assets are suggested because they can be easily and objectively measured and are a good proxy for income, which is difficult to assess (detailed proposals for setting up an asset-based welfare indicator can be found in World Bank 1995). Although growth monitoring to measure PEM is much more difficult to carry out, there is no alternative to setting up high-quality, community-based growth monitoring if parents are to become aware of and respond effectively to this major national problem (see Chapter 3). PEM is another good proxy for health, economic, and social disadvantage, and PEM status can be measured more easily at the community level than morbidity.

Improving the quality of growth monitoring on a nationwide basis will take five or six years. In the meantime, it is important to invest in a national survey of nutritional status that has validity below the regional level; regionally based data are not very useful for planning because, since devolution, the region is no longer a unit for political decisionmaking. A UNICEF-financed nutrition survey is already under way in twenty provinces; it would be useful to extend this to national coverage. Cost considerations argue for such surveys to be limited to the provincial level, with efforts to obtain municipal-level data on PEM to await the development of more reliable statistics on services.

Priorities for Intervention Programs

The data on child health, nutrition, and psychosocial development summarized in this chapter suggest that the main priorities should be programs for:

- Child survival, with special attention to maintaining the Expanded Program on Immunization, acute respiratory infection control, oral rehydration therapy, and interventions aimed at neonatal mortality
- Disease control, with special attention to diarrhea and pneumonia nationally, and to malaria, schistosomiasis, and helminth control in heavily endemic areas
- Deficiency control, for iron, vitamin A, and iodine among pregnant and lactating women as well as children
- PEM control programs, focusing on food security and behavioral change and on pregnant and lactating women as well as children

- Early education, for disadvantaged children (however, the lack of hard data in this area makes it difficult to define the appropriate extent and type of intervention)
- Maternal care and birth-spacing, aimed at improving mothers' health and nutrition and reducing infant and child mortality and malnutrition
- Water supply and sanitation in areas where limited coverage leads to high diarrhea rates.

3. Government Policies, Goals, and Intervention Programs

This chapter summarizes the government's main policies and goals for the development of young children in the Philippines and reviews the main government intervention programs in health, nutrition, and psychosocial development (nongovernmental interventions are discussed in Chapter 4). Each program is discussed in terms of the structure and evolution of its service delivery, its impact, and the strengths and weaknesses of its design, and recommendations are made for improving its performance.

Only nationwide programs are reviewed here. In addition to these, there are several smaller-scale programs and projects that may have important lessons for the design of national interventions but which the team doing the report on which this book is based was unable to visit. These include the LAKASS Program of the National Nutrition Council and the Area-Based Child Survival and Development Program, which are briefly described in Sections H and I, respectively, of the supplement volume.

Child Development Policies and Goals

The Philippines has a set of laws and policies, including a national plan of action for children, that strongly support child development. The government's qualitative and quantitative goals for the survival, protection, and development of children are clear and ambitious.

Laws

Philippine law provides unambiguous support for child development as opposed to just child survival. In addition to setting out basic rights to adequate food, shelter, clothing, and protection, the Child and Youth Welfare Code (Presidential Decree 603) says that the child has "the right to a well-rounded development of his personality to the end that he may become a happy, useful and active member of society" (Article 3). It specifies (Article 9) that "the child shall be given adequate care, assistance and guidance through his various levels of growth, from infancy to early and later childhood." And in Article 87 it encourages the organization in each barangay of a local Council for the Protection of Children to promote, among other things, the establishment of day care centers.

The 1987 Barangay Level Total Development and Protection of Children Act mandated more explicit support for child development. It obliged the Department of Social Welfare and Development to appropriate funds for establishing and maintaining day care centers. The law specifies that these centers are to implement a child development program for preschoolers that includes, among other things, referral and support for pregnant mothers; monitoring of births and completion of immunization; growth monitoring and supplementary feeding for nutrition; day care for children of working mothers; and intellectual and mental stimulation for children. The 1991 Local Government Code, which provided the legal mandate for the devolution of many social sector services to local governments, made the day care service, formerly the responsibility of the Department of Social Welfare and Development, one of the frontline barangay services for which local governments were to ensure budget support.

The Philippine Council for the Welfare of Children, which is an attached agency of the Department of Social Welfare and Development, is mandated by law (Presidential Decree 603) to coordinate the implementation and enforcement of all laws promoting child and youth welfare and to formulate and evaluate policies, programs, and services for the general welfare and protection of youth.

The Philippine Plan of Action for Children

In 1990 the Philippines signed the International Convention on the Rights of the Child and endorsed the World Declaration on the Survival, Protection, and Development of Children. Subsequent to the 1990 World Summit for Children, the Council for the Welfare of Children produced a plan of action for children entitled "The Filipino Children: 2000 and Beyond," which details the Philippines' commitment to extending the coverage, and improving the quality, of the full range of programs affecting child development.

In addition to the objective of establishing a day care center in every barangay, the plan includes the following quantitative goals:

- Reduction of the infant mortality rate from 61 per 1,000 live births in 1990 to 37.6 by 2000
- Reduction in the prevalence of severely or moderately underweight preschoolers from 14 percent in 1990 to 7 percent by 2000
- Reduction in the rate of low birth weight to less than 10 percent
- Virtual elimination of the consequences of iodine deficiency disorders in hyperendemic areas
- Virtual elimination of vitamin A deficiency and its consequences, including night blindness
- Provision of low-cost medicine and promoting health insurance for children.

Health Intervention Programs

The Structure of Services

The Department of Health was responsible for almost all public sector health services before devolution in 1991. After devolution, the responsibility for implementing health services passed to the 60 cities, 77 provinces, and more than 1,500 municipalities. The role of the Department of Health is now confined to policy formulation, regulation, monitoring, training, technical assistance, and the ability to influence the priorities and performance of local governments through the provision of matching grants for the implementation of particular programs. The implications of devolution for both the Department of Health and the Department of Social Welfare and Development are discussed in more detail in Chapter 4.

A restructuring at Department of Health headquarters in 1994 should help to integrate both policy formulation and the development of projects and programs for child health. Eleven of the key services affecting children—in the areas of family planning, maternal and child health, and nutrition—are now under one under secretary, in charge of a newly created Office of Public Health. In the field, the Department of Health maintains fifteen regional offices, through which it performs its technical assistance, training, and monitoring functions for the local governments.

At the local government level, provincial governors and city and municipal mayors oversee health and other devolved services. Local health boards act as advisory committees to the local governments' chief executives and their councils. These boards include representatives of the local government health staff and of the

Department of Health; elected officials; and local NGO and community leaders. Most tertiary-level referral facilities for children—that is, the provincial and district hospitals, and the budgets to run them—have been devolved to the provincial governors. First- and second-level facilities—barangay health stations and rural health units—are the responsibility of the municipalities.

At the periphery, the key health worker is the rural health midwife, who is responsible for maternal and child health outreach services, as well as assisting with other disease control programs. In most provinces, a rural health midwife is available for about 5,000 people, or three to five barangays (villages). During the past five years, with support from the World Bank, the Department of Health has hired an additional 2,500 rural health midwives, increasing the national strength by more than 20 percent. The new rural health midwives have been posted to remote and poorer areas. In the majority of the twenty-five most-disadvantaged provinces (as defined by the Presidential Commission to Fight Poverty), the ratio of midwives to population is now about one for every 2,000 or 3,000 people.

Midwives are assisted by barangay health workers, who volunteer two or three hours a week at a barangay health station or rural health unit; encourage community participation in health campaigns; and provide health education in their village. The barangay health worker movement has received varying degrees of encouragement and support from different governments. The Ramos government aims at building up a network of effective barangay health workers at a ratio of one for every twenty families in rural areas and one for every fifty families in urban areas, where population densities are higher and access easier. It is hard to assess how many barangay health workers there are, because many barangay health workers recruited and trained by previous governments are no longer active. But as a rough estimate, in a typical barangay of about 1,500 people, about ten individuals might be identified as barangay health workers, of whom about half might be active workers.

About a quarter of the barangays in the Philippines have barangay health stations, simple clinics containing a few supplies and medicines and staffed by a rural health midwife. The barangay health station serves as the health center for the two to five barangays covered by the rural health midwife. Health problems of any seriousness are referred to the rural health unit, whose staff includes a doctor and a public health nurse. A rural health unit is available for a population of about 20,000 people; a typical municipality would have one or two of these facilities. District hospitals are often severely underfunded; in practice, therefore, the main referral point from the rural health unit for a seriously ill child would usually be the provincial hospital.

The Intervention Programs

The different child health intervention programs have had varying impact, depending on the levels of commitment and funding they have had, how hard their technology is to manage, and how long they have been established. The immunization program, which has a tried and tested technology, high commitment, and ample funding, has been by far the most successful. The diarrhea program, which also has a well-tried technology, although one that is harder to implement, has been the next most successful. The program to control acute respiratory infection and the family planning and maternal care programs have so far had less impact, for reasons discussed below.

IMMUNIZATION. By the mid-1980s the immunization program had expanded to include the six standard antigens, but a 1986 evaluation indicated that only 21 percent of children were fully immunized by that time. Subsequently, the world attention that UNICEF helped to focus on immunization in the mid-1980s and the issuance of a presidential proclamation calling for universal immunization galvanized attention and effort. "Fully immunized child" coverage rose to 80 percent by 1989 and 90 percent by 1993. This extraordinary success was made possible by a number of simultaneous inputs, including strong political commitment, good program management, a strengthened cold chain system, a well-developed training program, and an extremely effective interpersonal and mass media health education campaign. Another key strategy was the holding of national immunization days twice a year; these were very successful in 1993 and 1994. The immunization program's next target is to eliminate neonatal tetanus and polio by the end of 1995.

In the short term, the main constraints to achieving this next goal are the managerial and financial uncertainties posed by devolution. There are some worrying signs that the immunization program is faltering. Monitoring data show that, for most of the main vaccines, coverage levels in 1993 were 2 to 3 percent less than in 1992. Staff of the Department of Health regional office report that materials for service provision, such as syringes and needles, are in short supply; that attendance at training courses by field health personnel has decreased; and that supervisory and outreach visits have diminished because travel allowances have not been provided by local governments (the last two problems affect all the public health outreach programs). Measures to relieve these generic devolution-related constraints are discussed in Chapter 4. In brief, it is clear that there is a strong argument for the central government to continue supporting cost-effective "public good" services such as immunization if local governments are unable to sustain these programs effectively.

In the medium term, the integrity of the cold chain system will be a major concern because most of the cold chain equipment was installed in 1985 and is wearing out. A cold chain study planned for mid-1994 will provide detailed estimates of the rehabilitation needs, which are likely to be substantial before 2000.

CONTROL OF DIARRHEAL DISEASES. The program for the control of diarrheal diseases was launched in the early 1980s. It has two main thrusts—preventing diarrhea by promoting breastfeeding and hygienic practices, and managing diarrhea through the use of oral rehydration therapy (ORT). The program is primarily aimed at preschoolers because three-quarters of all deaths from diarrhea occur in this age group. The program expanded rapidly from 1986 to 1992. Diarrhea training units were established at the national and regional levels for training rural health midwives and other field personnel; diarrhea management was incorporated into the medical, nursing, and midwifery preservice training curricula; and private sector nurses and doctors were oriented in diarrhea management through their professional associations. A procurement and logistics system was developed to ensure that ORT was available at all service outlets.

The information available does not permit as good an evaluation of the impact of the program to control diseases as is possible for immunization. The Department of Health is assessing the program's impact on mortality. There appears to have been a reduction in the prescription of antibiotics and the use of intravenous fluids and antidiarrheal preparations and a corresponding increase in the use of ORT for the management of diarrhea. ORT use has been variously measured at 49.5 percent (the 1993 Demographic and Health Survey) and 60 percent (the Department of Health's 1992 cluster surveys), the latter figure being an increase from only 15 percent in 1985. Also, public hospitals are reporting lower admissions of cases of diarrhea, and the number of reported deaths from diarrhea has been falling since 1990.

The program plan for the control of diarrheal diseases was updated in late 1993. In the future, particular emphasis will be given to home management of diarrhea and to morbidity reduction through the promotion of the seven interventions recommended by WHO for preventing diarrhea. However, sustaining and building on the program's achievements will be difficult. Sustaining past levels of achievement, given the uncertainties posed by devolution, will be a bigger challenge than for immunization, because the program to control diarrheal diseases is more difficult to manage: immunization lends itself to short national campaigns, whereas the control of diarrheal diseases requires the behavioral change of mothers on a day-to-day basis. And with regard to the proposed new emphases of the program, no financing strategy has yet been developed for the considerable additional resources required. Nor have the cost requirements been fully determined for the diarrhea morbidity reduction program—a key intervention if the Department of Health's efforts for children are to be reoriented toward child development as well as child survival.

CONTROL OF ACUTE RESPIRATORY INFECTIONS. Although pneumonia is the major killer of children, in the Philippines as in other countries the program for the control of acute respiratory infections was the last to be developed, because it was only in the late 1980s that tried, cost-effective technologies for field-level implementation became available. The program was launched five years ago, when various protocols were developed: a standard pneumonia detection protocol for use in homes and health facilities, a protocol for managing pneumonia, and standards for providing services at health facilities. Aside from the protocols, the main inputs of the program are training; drugs, medicines, and supplies for case management; a referral system; and a monitoring and evaluation system.

The accomplishments in training have been impressive, with 80 percent of rural health midwives, public health nurses, and doctors and 30 percent of public hospital clinicians trained in the new protocols. However, the current monitoring system does not permit a determination of how far the new case management system is being followed in the field. There is also a need for surveillance to monitor trends in incidence. The Department of Health is seeking technical assistance to review the control of acute respiratory infections and to help prepare the next five-year plan to develop the program further. Financing for this expanded program is uncertain, and, even at the current level of effort, problems of drug availability are emerging. USAID and World Bank assistance from ongoing projects for the control of acute respiratory infections and for other child survival interventions was scheduled to come to an end in late 1994 or early 1995.

FAMILY PLANNING, WOMEN'S HEALTH, AND SAFE MOTHERHOOD. In contrast to the weak commitment to and underfunding of family planning and maternal care during the 1980s, the Department of Health has made the program for family planning, women's health, and safe motherhood its flagship program and is implementing two major projects totaling more than ₱7 billion ($140 million) to support its development. Issues and plans related to family planning, maternal care, and safe motherhood are reviewed in detail in World Bank (1991) and (1994c) and are not repeated here.

As indicated in Chapter 2, efforts to strengthen maternal care and family planning services under the above projects should significantly, though indirectly, affect infant mortality. However, these projects do not include specific interventions to directly reduce the 35 percent of infant deaths that occur in the perinatal period, the time soon after childbirth. Work is needed to identify which of the leading causes of perinatal death can realistically be tackled and to develop the case management protocols and input requirements for doing so. These protocols will need to be introduced into the training curricula to be developed for field health staff and traditional birth attendants under the above projects, because perinatal services for infants must be delivered as an integral part of delivery and postpartum care. Similarly, mothers who are likely to give birth at home will need to be trained in how to identify and refer at-risk babies; this training should be an integral part of the health education they will receive during prenatal contacts with health staff.

Workloads, Service Integration, and Targeting

The rural health midwife's workload has increased significantly in recent years, with intensified implementation of the programs for immunization and the control of diarrheal diseases; the addition of the program to control acute respiratory infections; and continuing responsibilities to assist the control programs for malaria, tuberculosis, and schistosomiasis. The workload problem will be further exacerbated now that the major new family planning, women's health, and safe motherhood projects have begun. Barangay health workers can take on some of the work of community mobilization and health education, but their time inputs are limited because they are volunteers, and their limited skills mean they can make little contribution to delivering services. For example, a rural health midwife's skills are required for prenatal, obstetric, and postpartum care; prescription of oral contraceptives; and the insertion and follow-up of intrauterine devices—all activities likely to increase substantially in the next few years.

This growing problem implies the need to carefully review the ratio of field staff to population and to plan more systematically how the rural health midwife's time should be used and how the workload should be divided among her, the barangay health workers, and doctors and nurses at the rural health center. With regard to the first need, data are currently available only for the ratios of rural health midwives to population by province. There are no data by municipality, nor is it known whether rural health midwives are well distributed in relation to their target population within any given administrative area. A mapping exercise to determine this is required. It will be especially important to determine whether local governments are maintaining rural health midwives in remoter areas, where demands for service may be less vocal than in the towns.

Adopting the life-cycle approach to integrating and targeting services offers important potential gains in efficiency and effectiveness. Under this approach (see Section G in the supplement volume), fieldworkers would focus on clients who are most at risk, and at the times in their lives when they are most at risk. This means a systematic focus on pregnant and lactating women and children in the first five years of life, with particular attention to the first two years of life, when malnutrition and infection peak. During the regular contacts with this priority client group, field staff would provide a full range of services, rather than focusing on one particular program, or the current health education campaign, as has often happened in the past.

The life-cycle approach uses time more efficiently by focusing scarce resources on those most in need and by reducing unnecessary contacts with at-risk families through integrating service provision at each contact. This is also a more effective way to provide public health care from a human perspective, because clients are treated in a family context and in a holistic manner, rather than as immunization cases or malnutrition cases. But reorganizing services in this way has major implications for the redesign of service protocols, health education messages, training programs, and management information systems, as well as field work routines. Accordingly, the Department of Health plans to move ahead with the life-cycle approach on a pilot basis under the Urban Health and Nutrition Project, assisted by the World Bank and the Australian

International Development Assistance Bureau, and the Women's Health and Safe Motherhood Project, financed by a consortium. Successful implementation of this effort will be a key precondition for local governments to be able to manage a more intensive child health development effort, on top of the planned efforts to improve women's health and intensify other programs.

Conclusions

With the exception of interventions to reduce deaths in the first month of life, where prevention and case management protocols need to be carefully reviewed, the technical strategies for the key child health interventions are well developed. The main constraints facing the program are institutional and financial. On the institutional side, two constraints stand out. First, there are worrying signs that, at least under some local governments, delivery of public health services, including child health services, has been faltering since devolution. Strategies for dealing with this generic problem are discussed in Chapter 4. Second, rising workloads for field staff require a review of staffing ratios and a redesign of approaches to targeting and delivering services if additional investment in child health is to be absorbed and used effectively.

On the financial side, it must be recognized that at the time of devolution, local governments inherited a series of child health programs that were at different stages of development and effectiveness and that still suffered overall from the 1980s legacy of underfunding of primary care. Only the immunization program was fully developed. The program for the control of diarrheal diseases had reached perhaps half of its full potential, and the acute respiratory infection, maternal-perinatal care, and family planning programs lagged far behind. Substantial additional financing is required to achieve the nation's child health goals, yet large-scale USAID and World Bank projects financing child health interventions are ending. Chapter 5 attempts a rough estimate of the needs and discusses the prospects for raising financing from local government, the central government, and overseas aid sources.

Nutrition Intervention Programs

The Structure of Services

The structure of the Philippine nutrition program is more complicated than that of the health program because at least eight agencies have been involved on a major scale. The National Nutrition

Council, which is an attached agency of the Department of Agriculture, is the overall policymaking, coordinating, and monitoring body and coordinates a substantial nutrition intervention program of its own, LAKASS (see Section H of the supplement volume). The Department of Health is responsible for the micronutrient program, growth monitoring, nutrition education, and food supplementation of pregnant and lactating women and children under 3. The Department of Social Welfare and Development includes nutrition in its day care program for 4- to 6-year-olds. CARE, Catholic Relief Services, and the Diocesan church program provide large-scale food aid for supplementary feeding in the PEM control programs of the Department of Health and the Department of Social Welfare and Development. The Department of Agriculture's extension program promotes home gardens. The National Food Authority runs a generalized subsidy program for rice. And many NGOs are involved in nutrition projects on a smaller scale.

Local governments are the main actors in nutrition, as they are in health. At the local government level, nutrition activities are overseen by an intersectoral Nutrition Sub-Committee reporting to the Social Development Committee of the local government council. At the periphery, the same rural health midwives, barangay health workers, and day care workers who are responsible for child health and preschool development are also responsible for nutrition. They are assisted by barangay nutrition scholars, a cadre created by the National Nutrition Council more than fifteen years ago. About 1,000 new barangay nutrition scholars were trained each year during 1988–93 to increase coverage in deprived inner-city areas. Barangay nutrition scholars now number about 14,000, or about one for every three barangays. Like barangay health workers, barangay nutrition scholars average a couple of hours a day on nutrition work, ranging from helping with growth monitoring and supplementary feeding, to micronutrient distribution and nutrition education. Barangay nutrition scholars are compensated with accident insurance and an allowance that in most parts of the country ranges from ₱30 to ₱50 (less than $2) a month; in exceptional cases, such as the relatively well-off Cebu City, the allowance can be as much as ₱1,000 ($36).

Micronutrient Deficiency Control

Interventions against micronutrient deficiency can be divided into corrective interventions (routinely administered supplements), maintenance interventions (fortification of dietary staples), and promotional interventions (to increase the cultivation and consumption of micronutrient-rich foods). These approaches have different time horizons. The first can lead to significant reductions in prevalence within two years of effective implementation. The second can maintain the gains from corrective measures and help to accelerate prevalence declines. Ideally, permanent resolution of micronutrient deficiency problems lies with the third approach, but this is also the hardest and slowest to implement, because of the difficulty of educating people to change long-held dietary habits. Food fortification has therefore become a long-term intervention in many developed countries, where it is pursued through an industrial policy framework in which governments provide the private sector with incentives to fortify.

SUPPLEMENTATION. The Department of Health has given very high priority to attacking micronutrient deficiency and has succeeded in gaining strong political support for its efforts. A campaign approach has been used very effectively to increase coverage levels for vitamin A and iodine supplements to about 80 percent for the high-risk population groups. In 1993 a National Micronutrient Day with a major publicity campaign was used to distribute retinol (vitamin A) to all preschool children and iodine to preschool children and women of childbearing age. In 1994, National Immunization Days were used to distribute retinol along with measles vaccine to infants and to give follow-up doses to older age groups. With continued commitment from the Department of Health and local governments, the campaign approach promises to make major inroads into iodine and vitamin A deficiencies. However, given the difficulties of measuring subclinical levels of deficiency in the field, it is important to establish an effective sentinel surveillance system to monitor the actual impact of the program in risk groups with different characteristics, in addition to tracking program success by monitoring inputs.

Organizing an effective iron supplementation program is much more difficult, because iron supplements need to be taken daily or weekly, rather than twice a year or every two or three years, as in the case of vitamin A and iodine. Iron supplementation cannot therefore be tackled through the relatively easy-to-manage campaign approach. Given that iron supplementation has some negative side effects and leads to little visible or immediate positive change in well-being, persuading mothers to supplement themselves and their children regularly requires frequent contact and a strong relationship of trust between fieldworker and client. So far, the Department of Health's maternal care program has not succeeded in developing the regular contact and the quality of health education that is required. This is a major goal of the Women's Health and Safe Motherhood Project, as is improvement of the logistics system for supplying supplements. The introduction of longer dosage intervals is presently being considered, which, if adopted, should also make this intervention more acceptable to clients.

As indicated in Chapter 2, the very high level of iron deficiency among infants and children is a particular cause for concern. Because the maternal iron supplementation program has not yet been well implemented, it is unclear how far improving iron stores among mothers will reduce the deficiency among infants and children. In the interim, until the planned efforts to improve the maternal iron program have been implemented and evaluated, it makes sense to continue at least to give liquid iron supplements to infants with low birth weights, because these are the children at greatest risk. However, the high cost and additional managerial complexity of giving supplemental iron to all infants 6 months to 11 months old and to all preschool children with PEM, as currently proposed, may not be justified; few countries have reckoned this intervention to be cost-effective.

An important complement to iron supplementation against anemia can be the control of parasitic diseases, where these are highly prevalent. It is unclear how far parasites contribute to anemia in different population groups of children in different parts of the country. Geographic information system technology, which is currently being introduced in the Philippines, offers the potential of overlaying data for the prevalence of anemia and different types of parasitism to define which areas should be chosen for intensive efforts to control parasites. It is likely, for example, that it would be cost-effective to introduce routine intestinal deparasitization in certain populations rather than to treat children on clinical criteria alone, as is now done.

FORTIFICATION. Despite much research and some experimentation, fortification has not so far been implemented on a large scale for any of the three main micronutrients. The government is committed to doing much more in this area. The salt iodization program, begun in four areas of the country in 1981 but not sustained, will be reinitiated, with special priority for the endemic Cordillera region. Quality assurance testing is about to begin of iodized iron produced in two plants. Experimentation is also ongoing with community-based iodization of local water supplies. Procter & Gamble, which has 95 percent of the margarine market, is fortifying margarine with vitamin A. The government is also discussing large-scale fortification of rice, milk, and flour with this vitamin. The Food and Nutrition Research Institute developed technology for iron fortification of rice some years ago, but this has not been implemented on a large scale.

The Department of Health has been given the responsibility for organizing the micronutrient fortification program. The department is highly committed to the effort, but faces two major constraints. The first is the additional workload of organizing the variety of fortification projects proposed, on top of plans to intensify other micronutrient and PEM control activities. The second is the lack of specialized skills in an area that poses difficult technical, institutional, legal, and marketing challenges and that involves the Department of Health in negotiations in the unfamiliar environment of private industry. A combination of these constraints has resulted in a somewhat piecemeal approach to the fortification program; ad hoc negotiations with individual producers have substituted for well-thought-out industrywide plans. If the fortification program is to unfold as the government hopes, the Department of Health should be enabled to draw on technical assistance from countries that have already been successful in this area, and an institutional development plan should be prepared to ensure that the capacity is there to design, monitor, and evaluate the effort.

PROMOTION OF DIETARY CHANGE. The Department of Agriculture supports a home gardening program encouraging the cultivation of micronutrient-rich vegetables and fruits. It is planned to expand this effort by developing school and community biointensive gardens. Also proposed in the Philippine Plan of Action for Nutrition is a revamped program of social marketing to encourage people to eat foods that are rich in micronutrients or that increase the absorption of micronutrients, as do fruits and fats. An initial step in this program was the campaign to promote the cultivation and consumption of malanggay as part of the 1993 National Micronutrient Day.

Although the campaign approach is a valuable one, the difficulty of changing dietary habits means that it must be complemented with interpersonal health education efforts tailored to local diets and practices and to individual families' situations in terms of income and access to land. Much remains to be done to develop a sound social marketing strategy at this level and to incorporate appropriate communication efforts into fieldworkers' daily routines. With intensification planned for so many of the Department of Health's programs for women and children, there is a danger that efforts to encourage dietary change will be lost among more immediate priorities, thus prolonging clients' dependence on micronutrient supplementation programs. Given the emerging overload of field staff, and the difficulty of promoting dietary change, it is realistic to focus health education in each local area on just one or two dietary changes selected for their priority and local practicability.

The Department of Health and DSWD Programs to Control PEM

GROWTH MONITORING AND PROMOTION (GMP). Most PEM in the Philippines is moderate rather than severe and hence is not easily detected by the untrained eye. Growth monitoring is an essential tool for demonstrating to parents, first, that their child is malnourished; second, how quickly children's weights can decline in response to illness or underfeeding; and third, how quickly children can be brought back onto a normal growth path through better care and through feeding relatively small additional amounts of food. But although a valuable consciousness-raising and educational tool, GMP is not easy to implement. As a major international review recently concluded (Cervinskas, Gerein, and George 1992), GMP programs require careful technical design and strong training and supervisory support if they are to be effective; if poorly planned and supported, GMP programs are as bad as no program at all.

Two approaches to growth monitoring have so far been tried in the Philippines. Neither has worked well. The Under-Six Clinic Program of the Department of Health was started by the Nutrition Service in 1975 as a growth-monitoring initiative and was moved to the Maternal and Child Health Service in 1983 with the aim of making it an integrating mechanism for all health services for young children. Under this program, mothers are encouraged to bring their children to the barangay health station or rural health center for monthly weighing, at which time health and nutrition education, immunization, and other services are delivered. Support for this approach has been weak, perhaps because the Department of Health management has seen GMP as a strategy rather than a program in its own right. GMP has had no budget of its own (the nutrition budget of the Department of Health before devolution was less than half a percent of the departmental budget). Training programs have been weak because procedural manuals were not developed. And monitoring indicators for this activity have not been included in the management information system, thus reducing the incentive for implementation. As a result, many parents have no growth charts, charting is often irregular or of poor quality, and growth monitoring is seldom used by fieldworkers as an effective tool for promoting growth.

The second approach to growth monitoring, Operation Timbang, is a nutritional screening program that takes place once a year. It is implemented on a campaign basis, with the help of the rural health midwives, barangay nutrition scholars, and barangay health workers. Although Operation Timbang has helped to raise awareness of PEM problems, it is generally agreed that the nutrition data produced by Operation Timbang have been of poor quality, both because many of the scales used were faulty and because of inadequate worker training. But even if these problems are corrected, Operation Timbang cannot substitute for a more regular growth monitoring and promotion program as an intervention against PEM. An annual intervention is too infrequent to catch most children in nutritional trouble and cannot educate parents by demonstrating monthly weight gains.

Two approaches to reorienting the GMP program have been advocated, but these also do not promise to work well. In 1991 the Nutrition Service of the Department of Health drafted a plan for a community-based nutrition program that would center on monthly growth monitoring by barangay health workers of all children 0 to 60 months old. Good-quality implementation of such a plan is unlikely. On the one hand, if the Department of Health succeeds in increasing the number of barangay health workers so that there is one for every twenty families, about forty barangay health workers would monitor growth in an area typically covered by a rural health midwife—a number impossible to train and supervise adequately. On the other hand, if the number of active barangay health workers remains small, the workload of GMP, with more than 225 preschoolers in a typical barangay, would be more than can reasonably be expected of part-time volunteer workers. Aside from being unmanageable, attempting to provide monthly GMP to children 37 months to 60 months old would be a difficult "curative" intervention: most of these children are stunted, and the nutritional damage would be hard to undo.

Because of the difficulty of organizing good-quality GMP through the barangay health worker cadre, an alternative proposal has been to have monthly GMP carried out by the rural health midwife to ensure good quality and to restrict it to infants. In that it targets the younger age group, this is a more desirable "preventive" approach. But it is unclear whether educational contacts limited to the first year of life will be adequate to fully reorient mothers' feeding and care behaviors through the peak period of wasting, which extends well past the first year of life (Figure 2-10). Nor are rural health midwives likely to be able to implement even this restricted GMP program effectively. Past experience suggests that mothers will not bring their infants to the clinic a dozen times in a year. Yet the rural health midwife, with 60 to 150 infants to care for (depending on the size of her area), will have little time for outreach GMP work, given her growing responsibilities for improving child survival and prenatal and obstetric care.

It is therefore recommended that the growth promotion program for children under 6 be reoriented from a clinic to an outreach approach, with monthly monitoring and counseling carried out in the barangay, and that monthly growth monitoring be targeted on children during the peak period of wasting, that is, the first 24 or 36 months of life (Figure 2-10), with only quarterly monitoring for older preschoolers. The workload and staffing implications of targeting good-quality "preventive" growth promotion on the high-risk 0- to 24-month age group are discussed below.

FOOD SUPPLEMENTATION. About a million preschoolers a year have participated in three main supplementary feeding programs, one organized by the Department of Health with assistance from CARE, covering about 334,000 children, and the others supervised by the Department of Social Welfare and Development, through Catholic Relief Services, covering about 275,000 children, and through the Diocesan church, covering about 386,000 children. Most of the food for these programs has been supplied by the U.S. government as part of PL 480 food aid. USAID plans to phase out its PL 480 support for the Philippines over a two-year period, partly in response to priorities for assistance in Sub-Saharan Africa, and partly because of the perceived ineffectiveness of the Philippine supplementary feeding program and the nutrition program of which it is part. This rapid phase-out will force a radical reappraisal of the supplementary feeding program, a task that was initiated in late 1993 by a committee chaired by the National Nutrition Council and composed of staff representatives from the National Nutrition Council, the Department of Health, and the Department of Social Welfare and Development.

Several design problems have constrained the effectiveness of the supplementation program. First, the foods offered were those that the United States could spare, not necessarily the best weaning foods or those most suited to local tastes. Second, much of the food went to older children, rather than those at the peak ages for wasting, many of whom were not covered by the program. Third, much of the food was distributed on a "take home" basis, so that an unknown quantity was shared with older family members. Finally, depending on the implementing agency, children might stay in the feeding program for six to twenty-four months, thus encouraging dependency on food assistance from outside the family. Program designers were ambivalent, and clients did not understand, as to whether supplementary feeding was a growth promotion intervention designed to educate parents about better childcare or a food security intervention providing a safety net for the very poor.

Because the withdrawal of PL 480 support will require much tighter targeting of scarce resources, it provides an opportunity to rethink the supplementary feeding program's technical design. Four changes are recommended, corresponding to the constraints summarized above.

- Substituting locally produced weaning foods of a required quality, suited to local tastes
- Tightly targeting supplementation on nutritionally at-risk pregnant women (to combat low birth weight) and on children ages 6 months to 24 months or 6 months to 36 months whose growth is faltering or who are moderately or severely malnourished
- Feeding children on-site to ensure that they actually get the supplement intended for them
- Restricting the time children spend in the supplementation program to three to six months and accompanying supplementation with intensive education on better care and feeding in the home; this will discourage dependency by sending the message to parents that the food supplementation program is a short-term, educational effort, seeking to improve but not substitute for the parents' own childcare efforts.

Food supplementation designed along the above lines can be an important complement to nutrition education, because it enables parents to see, from the growth chart, the difference that additional small amounts of food can make. But the amount of supplement provided, typically 300–400 kilocalories, or no more than a third of a child's requirements, is not enough—nor is it intended to be enough—to fill the food gap in a food-insecure household. It is essential for nutrition policy to distinguish between food supplementation, which should be seen not as a "dole" but as a short-term, educational intervention integral to the child growth promotion program, and food subsidy, which may need to be provided for a much longer term to a limited number of the very poor. Food subsidies are discussed separately below.

WORKLOAD AND STAFFING IMPLICATIONS. Given the importance of poor caring practices as a cause of PEM (Chapter 2), it seems unlikely that the Philippines can rapidly reduce moderate PEM to acceptable levels without retargeting and redesigning its growth promotion and supplementary feeding program along the above lines. Successfully managing such a program requires a lot a time from fieldworkers. For example, in a typical barangay of 1,500 people, there are 35 to 45 pregnant and lactating women and 70 to 90 children 0 to 24 months old at any given time. The experience of other countries suggests that the time implications of running a good-quality growth promotion program at the village level are often underestimated. The lesson from the Tamil Nadu Nutrition Program in India—one of a very few high-quality growth promotion efforts in Asia—is that good growth charting and counseling takes about three days a month; that running an on-site supplementary feeding and counseling program takes two to three hours a day, six days a week; and that home visits and record-keeping account for an additional two to three hours a day.

The staffing issue to be resolved is whether it will be more cost-effective to entrust this work to a single paid worker in each barangay, who would work four to six hours a day on GMP or to divide responsibility for GMP among several volunteer barangay health workers, each working fewer hours. The first option is strongly recommended. The time and dedication required to run GMP effectively are significant. Because the workload has to be sustained daily, it cannot be compared to the intensive but brief time contributions to immunization and micronutrient campaigns, in which volunteer workers have been most successful in the past. Paying an incentive commensurate for work done is first of all equitable, an important consideration in barangays where volunteers are themselves poor. Second, and equally important, payment allows program managers to hold workers accountable for performance.

Aside from the drawbacks of inequity and lack of accountability, the use of volunteers poses problems related to the management and cost of training and supervision. Because good-quality growth monitoring and counseling are difficult and require careful training and intensive follow-up, and because rural health midwives are themselves increasingly overloaded, it will be very difficult for one rural health midwife to provide effective support for more than three or four GMP workers, that is, one for each barangay. The idea that employing larger numbers of volunteers for outreach work is a cheap way of organizing GMP may be illusory. The high dropout rate of volunteers in the barangay health worker program and hence the constant need to train new workers would add significantly to the workload and cost of program support.

Food Security Interventions

Broader policies affecting food security, such as the macroeconomic framework and the government's antipoverty program, are beyond the scope of this book. Here discussion is limited to a few important policy issues that directly affect young children with regard to the two main government interventions in food security. These are livelihood creation programs and the food subsidy program run by the National Food Authority. This section also outlines the kind of targeting and coordination that will be needed at the barangay and municipal levels to ensure that food security interventions reach those most in need. More general proposals for developing a safety net to ensure the food security of the very poor are discussed in detail in World Bank (1995).

LIVELIHOOD PROGRAMS. The government has made livelihood creation the centerpiece of its strategy to reduce poverty (Philippine Institute of Development Studies 1993). Analyzing the strengths and weaknesses of current and proposed livelihood-creation interventions would be a very substantial task, given the large number of programs fragmented among many implementing agencies and the difficult issues of equity and cost-effectiveness. Such an analysis is beyond the scope of a book dealing only with young children. Nevertheless, the types of livelihood programs the government chooses, and the relative priority given to livelihood programs as against other interventions, will significantly affect child development. Three issues stand out.

First, research in a number of countries has shown that it is not just increases in employment and household income that are important to improving food security but who controls additional income; income going to mothers is often more likely to improve children's welfare than income going to fathers. This finding has been corroborated for the Philippines in a study by Senauer, Garcia, and Jacinto (1988) indicating that an increase in husbands' wages increases the calorie allocation to husbands and wives but reduces the share of the family food basket going to children. Increases in women's wages increase the share of family calories going to children. This strongly suggests that those designing livelihood programs in the Philippines should favor interventions increasing women's employment and incomes if the concern is for child welfare as well as overall economic growth.

Second, several agencies, disappointed with the lack of success of growth monitoring and food supplementation programs in the Philippines, are thinking of increased investment in livelihood programs as a substitute. Although livelihood creation is an important complement to a good GMP program, it cannot substitute for such a program, because, as has been shown for the Philippines, extra income will not deal with poor caring practices that are such an important cause of malnutrition in children under 3 (Chapter 2). In the food-insecure families studied by Senauer, for example, although the whole family ate less than the recommended daily allowance of calories, husbands ate 81 percent, wives ate 78 percent, and children ate only 64 percent of the daily allowance. Filipinos have a well-deserved reputation for caring for children; this relative deprivation of children is presumably because parents do not readily appreciate the rapid change in protein and energy requirements at this age, nor can they easily detect the first stages of malnutrition. Unless the Philippines develops a good, complementary GMP program that demonstrates malnutrition, income increases from livelihood programs will have less effect than they otherwise might on the nutritional status of children.

Finally, there are important equity concerns about too great a reliance on livelihood creation to alleviate poverty and malnutrition. Evidence from many countries shows that new jobs go last or not at all to the poorest, who, as the least educated and often the most remote, are least able to take advantage of opportunity when it comes. Even though new jobs are the engine for economic growth and poverty reduction in the medium and long terms, there is a strong case for developing a safety net to protect the nutritional status of the very poor, and their children, in the short term. One possible intervention for this purpose is discussed briefly in the next section.

FOOD SUBSIDIES. The National Food Authority's mandate is to improve the food security of the consumer and to stabilize producer prices. Its impact on food security is discussed in detail in World Bank (1995). In brief, the National Food Authority spends P2 billion to P3 billion ($71 million to $107 million) a year to finance a generalized subsidy for rice sold through retail outlets. However, because this rice has represented only 2 to 11 percent of consumption, its effects on the market have not been big enough to substantially affect prices. Because the subsidy has been general, that is, spread thinly and not targeted specifically on poor consumers, the income transfer to the poor, as to other consumers, has represented only about P2.60 ($0.09) for each kilo of rice, and this saving has come at a very high administrative cost, equaling the cost of the subsidy for each kilo. Moreover, the geographic distribution of subsidized rice has not been equitable; for example, the National Capital and the Cordillera regions, which together contain only 3.5 percent of the subsistence poor, received more than 40 percent of the National Food Authority rice in 1993. Altogether, the National Food Authority has been evaluated as both ineffective and inefficient at improving the food security of the poor.

From the perspective of improving the nutritional status of young children, two more targeted uses for the funds now spent on the National Food Authority would have a high payoff. The first would be to redirect funds to substitute for the withdrawal of PL 480 food aid for children and to revamp the GMP program so that it operates more effectively. The second would be to finance a new, tightly targeted food subsidy scheme, probably by providing food stamps, to alleviate the food insecurity of the poorest families, who are unlikely to get access to additional employment in the short and medium terms. Ways to design and target such a program are discussed in World Bank (1995). Of these two programs, the first appears to be the priority, both because it will be more immediately cost-effective to strengthen an existing program in which there are sunk costs than to start a new one and because no other PEM intervention is likely to be successful until a good growth monitoring program is in place and parents perceive that their children are malnourished. But a food security intervention, such as a food stamp scheme, will also be needed for the protection and development of children whose families, however well they are educated in childcare, do not have the money to feed them properly. GMP and food security interventions should be implemented together.

TARGETING AND COORDINATING FOOD SECURITY INTERVENTIONS. Careful thought will need to be given to the processes required at the barangay and municipal levels to identify families in need of food security interventions, to decide which kinds of interventions are most appropriate, and to coordinate the delivery of interventions. A process similar to UNICEF's "Triple A" process—assessment of the nutrition problem, analysis of its causes, and action to intervene—will need to be developed at the municipal level.

Assessment might be done by monthly growth monitoring and by surveying household assets for targeting purposes, as discussed in Chapter 2. Analysis would involve the combined judgment of the barangay worker and supervisors in health and social welfare about the relative importance of health, care, and food security as causes of malnutrition. Where food insecurity is a significant factor, action would involve deciding which mix of available interventions would be appropriate and working with the field staff of the relevant programs to ensure that the interventions are made available. For example, a family may need access to credit or livelihood programs to increase food security over the medium and long terms, but they may also need immediate access to a food subsidy program to reduce malnutrition until income-generating activities can successfully be established. Considerable further work is required to develop mechanisms for the integration of food security interventions at the local level, an issue that is revisited in Chapter 4.

Conclusions

The government's commitment to reducing micronutrient malnutrition is strong, and there is a real prospect of meeting the national goal of eliminating vitamin A and iodine deficiencies as a public health problem by 2000. It is less clear that currently planned measures to improve the iron supplementation program represent the most that can be done. Because anemia is the most common form of malnutrition in the Philippines, a further strategy review will be important. Enthusiasm to tackle micronutrient deficiency on all fronts has stretched the resources of the Department of Health's nutrition staff thinly, especially when it comes to working with industry to promote food fortification and to developing social marketing programs to support local government efforts to promote dietary change. If implementation of the medium- and long-term measures required to avoid continuing dependence on supplementation is not to lag behind, it will be important to strengthen the Department of Health's planning and support capacity in these areas and to ensure that the department can draw on the best program design experience from other countries. Probably no other investment opportunity offers such potential impact on children at such low cost as does strengthening the micronutrient malnutrition control program.

In contrast to its commitment and initiative in the area of micronutrient malnutrition, the government has mounted no comparable effort to improve the PEM control program. The growth monitoring and promotion program suffers from clear technical design problems and from being a low priority, and large sums of money continue to be wasted on a generalized food subsidy that does not provide a worthwhile safety net for the food insecure. Despite a continuing reduction in PEM rates, moderate malnutrition, as measured by international standards, still affects more than a quarter of preschoolers. And given the close links between PEM and child deaths, continuing slow progress in reducing PEM may also threaten the achievement of national mortality reduction goals.

The proposed rapid phaseout of PL 480 support—the GMP program's main financial resource—will presumably precipitate the program's reform. And there are signs that the government may be more willing to tackle the drain on public resources of the food subsidy program. It will be essential to use this opportunity to reform the nutrition program for the maximum benefit of pregnant women and young children, the most vulnerable members of society from a nutritional standpoint. Significant additional financing would be required, first, to revamp the GMP program (including the payment of allowances for fieldworkers and the replacement of food aid with domestic resources) and, second, to develop a targeted food security intervention for the poorest. At a time of severe fiscal constraints, this financing cannot come as an addition to public spending. Therefore, the National Food Authority's substantial expenditures on generalized food subsidies should be reallocated to strengthen and develop a more effective and efficient PEM control program.

Early Education

The Structure of Services

Before devolution, the Department of Social Welfare and Development was the main government agency involved in psychosocial developmental or early education services. The department developed two main programs in this area, aside from the food supplementation program discussed above: the Day Care Center Program and the Parent Effectiveness Service Program. The Day Care Center Program is by far the largest and is the main focus of discussion in this chapter. Its name is somewhat confusing because the program takes in children for only two to three hours a day and provides them with organized early education; it is therefore really a preschool education rather than a day care program. In addition, the Department of Education, Culture, and Sports provides preschool education for 6-year-olds, and the Department of Health has included a parent education component in its clinics for children under 6; the latter seems to have had little impact and is not reviewed here. A very large number of NGOs also provide preschool and day care services (see Chapter 4).

Since devolution, local government is mandated to provide the early education services previously provided by the Department of

Social Welfare and Development. As with the Department of Health, the role of the Department of Social Welfare and Development is now one of policy development, coordination, monitoring, training, and technical assistance. The department maintains a network of offices in the regions to carry out its support role. At headquarters, its activities for children are divided among three bureaus: the Bureau of Child and Youth Welfare, which supports the day care center program; the Bureau of Family and Community Welfare, which supports the parent effectiveness program (as well as running a livelihood-creation program for the very poor); and the Bureau of Emergency Assistance, which supports nutrition activities. The Department of Education, Culture, and Sports, however, has not been devolved, and its preschool activities are managed from Manila by the Bureau of Elementary Education.

At the city and municipal levels, the main worker is the social welfare officer, a graduate-level staff member responsible for looking after the full range of social welfare programs. These include emergency assistance, livelihood creation, beautification, and shelter programs, in addition to child development work. Depending on the size of the municipality, the number of social welfare officers can vary from one to three. Above the village level, therefore, the ratio of full-time, paid social welfare staff to clients is, on average, a quarter of that of the health service, which would have at least four rural health midwives and four health center staff in a typical municipality.

At the barangay level, the key worker is the day care worker, a full-time paraprofessional with a minimum of two years of college education. Although all day care workers do the same work, they differ very considerably in how much they are paid. Encadred workers are paid ₱2,000 to ₱3,000 ($70 to $105) a month. They are a small minority (less than 10 percent of day care workers) who were recruited in the initial phase of the day care center program in the 1980s. Recognizing that it did not have the budget for large-scale expansion of the program at these salary levels, the Department of Social Welfare and Development later moved to a less costly system of "volunteer" day care workers, who are paid allowances. Most local governments, who are now responsible for the day care workers, pay them no more than the ₱500 ($18) allowance per month mandated by law. This is supposed to be topped up with a contribution of about ₱250 ($9) a month from the community, although field visits suggest that community contributions are a fraction of this amount. In a few better-off municipalities, day care worker allowances paid by the local government may be as much as ₱1,000 ($36) a month.

The Day Care Center Program

Public provision of day care started as early as 1964 but began on a large scale only following passage of the 1978 Barangay Day Care Law. Government-run day care centers are designed for thirty children at a time, and hence, where morning and afternoon sessions are run, have a capacity for about sixty children; in practice, many run at far less than full capacity. The program is aimed at 4- to 6-year-olds. The length of each session is two hours, organized according to a standard curriculum of informal education and organized play, which was developed at the national level. The day care center program has expanded steadily in recent years, with an especially big jump in coverage after devolution (when local governments were mandated to provide this service). But the rapid expansion—from 13,900 centers in 1991 to more than 18,000 in 1992—was from a small base, so that in 1992 still only 43 percent of barangays in the country had a government-provided day care center.

Systematic training of day care workers began in 1983, when, with assistance from UNICEF, the Department of Social Welfare and Development launched the first Early Childhood Enrichment Program, which supported a needs assessment and a one-month training program for 1,000 day care workers a year. But by the end of the second phase of the program in 1987, only about 45 percent of the 12,000 day care workers existing at that time had been trained. To reduce the backlog, the emphasis shifted to a new program of twelve-day, on-the-job training, although the original training program was not discontinued. Under the new program, the number of trainers was increased by allowing selected day care workers to become trainers. By the end of 1992, when there were about 18,000 day care centers, about 12,500 day care workers had been trained. Of these about 4,300 had had the training as it was originally designed and 8,200 the on-the-job training (HEWSPECS 1994).

IMPACT AND QUALITY ISSUES. In the absence of a thorough evaluation of early education programs in the Philippines, or even a locally appropriate set of developmental standards for measuring performance (Chapter 2), it is impossible to assess the impact of the day care center program. However, there is general agreement, supported by observations made on field visits, that quality is low. Educational materials are in very short supply in most centers. Most local governments do not budget for these, and community contributions for them are seldom forthcoming. In many centers many of the materials that are in evidence have been paid for by the day care worker herself. Similarly, the child stimulation and teaching skills of many day care workers appear to be weak, and there is a tendency, common to many preschool programs around the world, for the day care workers to focus on initial instruction in the "three Rs" rather than on the organized play that is more developmentally appropriate for this age group. Anecdotal information suggests that the work of day care workers who have had only the on-the-job training is of significantly lower quality than that of those with the full training.

Several factors combine to cause low quality. First, the length of on-the-job training is insufficient for a good foundation, and the ability of day care workers to act as good trainers when they do not have trainer training is questionable. Second, large classes make good-quality stimulation and teaching difficult. Third, the limited numbers and heavy workload of social welfare officers make regular, good-quality supervision impossible. (The ratio of social welfare officers to day care workers is usually in the range of one to five or one to ten, depending on the number of barangays with a day care center in a particular municipality. Although ratios in this range would normally be considered reasonable for supervision, the many different programs for which social welfare officers are responsible leave them with limited time for the on-the-job training and supervision required by the day care center program.) Fourth, budget allocations by local governments for recurrent expenditures are low: allowances for day care workers are insufficient to act as incentives, and there are low or no budget allocations for educational materials. Allocations may be low because of inability to pay, lack of understanding of what constitutes acceptable quality and the minimum inputs to achieve it, or lack of interest (some local governments may be more interested in fulfilling the letter of the Day Care Law and reaping the political rewards of establishing new centers than in the quality of the services provided).

To bring the day care center program up to an acceptable level of quality, the following steps are suggested:

- Create an additional social welfare officer post in each municipality, a post dedicated to monitoring, supervising, and providing training for early childhood development (ECD) activities. (The need for this post will become still more pressing as local governments create more day care centers—the rapid rate of growth in numbers seen since devolution seems to be continuing.)

- Develop a training center in each region to provide social welfare officers who are in charge of day care centers with supervisory and trainer training.
- Define minimum standards for day care center quality, day care worker allowances, and materials and other inputs.
- Limit class size to twenty children a session (a number already stretching the limits for good-quality care).
- Develop a program in which local governments undertake to carry out agreed-upon improvements in quality in return for a package of technical, financial, and training assistance from the Department of Social Welfare and Development. (Possible ways to structure such a program are discussed in Chapter 4.)

COVERAGE, ACCESS, AND EQUITY. Coverage and equity concerns exist at two different levels—within the barangay (which families get services) and nationally (how equitably the expansion of the day care center program is spread across the country).

A typical barangay may have about ninety children who are 4 or 5 years old (it is assumed here that 6-year-olds will soon be absorbed by the expansion of elementary education and will no longer be potential clients of the day care center program). Of these ninety, no more than forty could be absorbed by one day care center if class size is reduced, as recommended above. There has been no study of the socioeconomic levels of children who attend public day care centers against those who do not go to an organized preschool, but field visits suggest that the very poor may be crowded out of the day care center system by the less poor.

If the public sector is to provide preschool services, these must reach the most disadvantaged children. A selection mechanism should be developed to ensure that the poorest are identified for access to the service. Obvious criteria for inclusion would be malnutrition, as shown by the growth monitoring program, and poverty, as shown by a family asset–based indicator that might be developed for access to the food stamp safety net program recommended above. Adherence to the inclusion criteria for the very poor could then become one of the conditions of local government access to an assistance package from the central government.

Such an approach might still not guarantee access for the very poor living at the peripheries of villages. Nor may day care centers in barangay centers be a convenient service point for scattered communities, for example, some indigenous communities. A home-based approach for the provision of early education may be more appropriate in these circumstances. This approach, although tried only on an experimental basis in the Philippines, has proved quite successful in several Latin American countries. In it, early education or day care services for six or seven neighborhood children are provided by a suitably qualified and trained local mother in her own home. Although this approach is recommended for ensuring that poor people living at the periphery get access to services, it is unlikely to be a cost-effective substitute for the center-based program as a whole. This is because the training and supervision requirements for such "satellite" centers would be almost as high as for day care centers serving forty children. Yet to serve forty children in each barangay, about six home-based centers would need to be established, or about seventy-five for each municipality, making the provision of good-quality support impossible.

Another dimension to the coverage and equity issue is the distribution of day care centers across the country and between municipalities. Unlike the health system, where the ratio of rural health midwives to clients is now better than average in almost all the poorer provinces, there are far fewer day care centers than average in several of the poorest regions, especially in Eastern Visayas and parts of Mindanao (Figure 3-1). And, although there are no data on

Figure 3-1. Percentage of Barangays with Day Care Centers, by Region, 1992

Percent

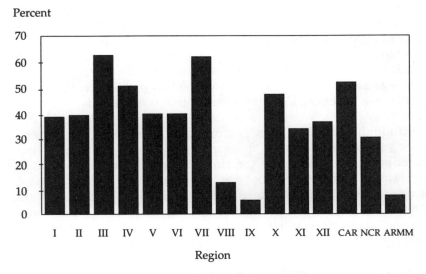

Region

Note: CAR, Cordillera Administrative Region; NCR, National Capital Region; ARMM, Autonomous Region of Muslim Mindanao.

Source: HEWSPECS (1994).

the distribution of day care centers opened since devolution, it is clear from field visits that there is also great variation within regions, with some municipalities having opened only one or two centers since devolution and others having neared full coverage. What determines the difference appears to be the interest of the local mayor and council in this activity rather than how well off the municipality is. A related policy issue is whether the central government should provide financial incentives for lagging regions and municipalities to develop their day care center networks. This issue is returned to in Chapter 5 in the context of discussion of the costs of improving the quality and expanding the coverage of the day care center program.

The Preschool Education Program

The Department of Education, Culture, and Sports has defined improvement of preschool education as one of four priority areas for improving the quality of primary education. Preschool has assumed particular importance in the Philippines because primary school has not begun until age 7. Concerned about the lack of school readiness of children coming into the system, the department issued a policy document in 1971 encouraging its school divisions to establish preschool classes. And in 1989, it issued a departmental order defining the standards for the organization and operation of preschools or kindergarten schools. The size of the department's preschool program is quite small. In 1990–91, it ran 2,888 preschool classes with 165,997 enrollees. Since 1990 the department has also been organizing summer preschools, in which the transition to formal school is eased by the integration of ECD activities during the first eight weeks of grade 1. Both programs use teachers and classrooms that are already with the department.

Although there has been no formal evaluation of the department's preschool program, a generally expressed concern is that the educational approach is too close to formal elementary schooling, largely because preschool classes are taught by primary school teachers steeped in traditional methods. The department has recently responded by creating in each region a core of preschool trainers whose job is to reorient the pedagogical approach. Also, in 1993 the department allocated ₱100 million (about $3.5 million) to begin a new community-based preschool program for 5- and 6-year-olds. It is not yet clear how this will be designed or how far it will expand. Given the uncertainties about the most cost-effective design for early education interventions (Chapter 1), experimentation with different approaches by both the Department of Social Welfare and Development and the Department of Education, Culture, and Sports is desirable. Nevertheless, several considerations argue against a rapid expansion of the new community-based preschool program, if, as proposed at the time the study leading to this book was made, it is to be limited to 5-year-olds.

Most countries have found the developmental needs of 5-year-olds better met by integrating them into preschool programs for 3- to 5-year-olds. It may also not be cost-effective to create a new program, which would require new teachers and buildings, for just 5-year-olds. And third, the department is about to embark on an extensive program to improve the quality of primary education as well as to extend it to 6-year-olds. Doing all this will severely limit the department's managerial capacity to develop a new program requiring substantial reorientation from traditional practice. Finally, as noted above, the department's traditional pedagogical approach affords it no comparative advantage in designing and implementing the proposed community-based preschool program. Given the high costs of creating a new infrastructure for the 5-year-olds, small-scale experimentation with the proposed community-based approach, together with a careful evaluation of relative cost-effectiveness, would be desirable. At the same time, although the day care center program currently suffers from poor technical support and underfinancing and hence is of low quality, the day care center program's integration of 3- to 5-year-olds, its informal educational approach, and its existing infrastructure all make it a suitable foundation for efforts to improve quality and expand coverage to the neediest children.

As the main "market" for preschoolers, the Department of Education, Culture, and Sports has a strong interest in the success of ECD; indeed, the success of departmental efforts to improve the quality of basic education will be affected by the success of the country's ECD program. The department should therefore have a strong presence in developing policy and in planning for any expansion or quality improvement of the ECD system. The Department of Education, Culture, and Sports and the Department of Social Welfare and Development should jointly address what standards should be set and how the curricula should be revised so as to provide a better-planned and smoother transition for children from informal preschool to formal school. This will require that ECD activities be incorporated into the curriculum to be developed for the 6-year-olds coming into primary school and that basic

Filipino and English language instruction be more systematically incorporated into learning and play activities at day care centers. The sudden switch out of the vernacular and into these languages in elementary school is a significant barrier to enjoyment and achievement in school for many poor children. A careful study of the psychosocial developmental status of children as they enter school, as proposed in Chapter 2, would help in reorienting the elementary education system to fit the needs of disadvantaged children entering the system.

The Parent Effectiveness Service Program

To improve parenting skills, in 1978 the Department of Social Welfare and Development initiated the Parent Effectiveness Service Program. Its main method of operation has been group discussion and instruction. These groups are led by day care workers and social welfare officers and consist of parents with preschool children, some of whom attend the day care center and some of whom do not. The department has developed twelve-session plans for this purpose, and the parents are encouraged to identify their own child-rearing needs and problems and to plan which topics should be discussed and in what sequence. A 1989 evaluation of the program concluded that social welfare staff were not adequately prepared to teach parents because they had not mastered the necessary skills themselves. These findings led to a revision of the curriculum. Also at about this time, to expand the coverage of this program, the department began to train parent volunteers who had shown interest and leadership qualities to become trainers. At present, coverage remains small, with only about 1,700 social welfare staff and 1,800 volunteers trained; the program probably has not affected more than 10 percent of the barangays. During 1993 a pilot test was carried out using radio to extend coverage. Lessons from the curriculum were aired, parents who were enrolled in the program were given assignments to try at home, and follow-up home visits were arranged by trained staff and volunteers.

To consolidate and review experiences with the program, and as mandated by the Child and Youth Welfare Code, Parent Education Congresses are conducted annually at barangay, municipal, provincial, and regional levels, with a national-level congress held every three years. However, no recent independent evaluation of the program is available. Because the education of parents and children needs to be integrated, it does not seem appropriate to have one bureau plan for this program and another bureau plan for the day care center program, as is done now.

Day Care for Working Mothers

The so-called day care center program does not actually address the day care needs of working mothers because its hours of operation are very limited. Nor, of course, does it attempt to address the needs of parents with children under four. But, as noted in Chapter 2, large and increasing numbers of mothers work outside the home, often where it is difficult or undesirable to bring the child to the workplace. The demand for services that combine the custodial care of children with appropriate education and stimulation is therefore rising. Two ways to provide daylong care, including early education, are factory-based and home-based day care.

Recently, there has been a modest breakthrough in the provision of day care services by factories for their female employees. Pioneer corporations have included the Philippines Association of Flour Millers, which has set up eight day care centers; Gelmart Inc., where day care for an 8,000-strong female work force was provided at the initiative of the employees' union; and Rubberworld and North Atlantic Garments, where day care was recently included for the first time in a collective bargaining agreement. These efforts have been supported by the Department of Social Welfare and Development and NGOs such as Arugaan, Save the Children (U.S.A.), and Parents' Alternatives. The spread of factory-based day care has been inhibited by economic recession and by the lack of effective support systems for factory-based initiatives once the decision to establish day care centers has been made. A question for the Department of Social Welfare and Development, to which the answer is unclear, is whether its staff should be increased to help meet these needs or whether they can adequately be met by the NGO community.

Most poor women do not work in factories and cannot afford institutionalized day care. The preferred form of day care for most families in the Philippines is therefore likely to be home-based care, along the lines suggested above for satellite day care centers. Experience from other countries indicates that the private sector can provide such care on a commercial basis (Chapter 1). As with factory-based care, the issue is whether social welfare workers should be involved in training and supporting home-based day care. The evidence in the Philippines is that commercial, home-based care systems for poor women are not emerging as the result of market forces and that poorer women with several preschoolers are more likely to work outside the home, often leaving their children with inadequate care arrangements (Chapter 2). There seems to be a case on equity grounds, therefore, for local government field staff to encourage and support the development of at least one home-based day care center for each barangay, with participation limited to members of the group of poor clients who are priorities for inclusion in the day care center program. Once this demonstration center is seen to be operating viably, market forces should lead to the establishment of others.

Conclusions

As with the psychosocial developmental status of preschoolers (Chapter 2), there has been almost no evaluation of the operational effectiveness of early education programs. It is now not possible to assess the impact of these programs. This situation needs to be remedied as a priority.

There should be a clear delineation of responsibility between government agencies for the implementation and support of early education programs. It is recommended that the day care center program of the Department of Social Welfare and Development be strengthened as the national public sector early education program, given its existing infrastructure covering more than a third of the country and the fact that it is de facto operating as a preschool rather than a day care program.

Despite the absence of a good impact evaluation, it is clear that the quality of the day care center program is very low. Most local governments are preoccupied with expanding the numbers of centers rather than seeing that they work well. Given the costs already sunk by the government in this program, which is mandated by law, additional investment to improve quality will have high returns. The reorientation required is significant, including improving the curriculum, reducing the number of children in a session, increasing the number and effectiveness of supervisors, improving the performance of day care workers through better training and supervision, increasing the allowance of day care workers to provide an incentive for performance, and agreeing on a level of inputs for day care centers that is the minimum required for acceptable quality. Introducing such changes will require that an assistance program for local governments be developed in which local governments undertake to improve quality in return for a package of technical, financial, and training assistance from the Department of Social Welfare and Development.

Although improving quality should be the first priority, early education services also need to be expanded in lagging regions and municipalities. Once the already existing day care centers are operating at an acceptable level of quality, consideration should be given to developing "satellite" home-based centers, which could both provide early education services for the 4- to 6-year-old children of very poor families living far from the barangay center and provide day care facilities for the 2- to 6-year-old children of poor, working mothers.

4. Creating an Integrated, National Early Childhood Development Program

The two previous chapters looked at problems and programs in health, nutrition, and psychosocial development separately because so far in the Philippines this is how these problems have mostly been seen and how the intervention programs have mostly been managed. This chapter sets out a vision of how an integrated national early childhood development program in the Philippines might look. It attempts to incorporate the "best practice" approaches to ECD summarized in Chapter 1 and at the same time to build on what already exists in the field rather than start from scratch with new service delivery systems that would be unaffordable and unacceptable. As is the nature of a sector review, the vision presented is broad and would need to be modified and fleshed out to turn it from a general proposal into a specific investment plan.

The first section of this chapter presents one vision of an ECD program model at the local level, looking at the core package of services that needs to be delivered, at the service delivery personnel required, at job content, at methods for targeting services on priority clients, at the needs for strengthening technical support and supervision, and at the desirability of experimentation with different approaches to delivering services, especially in early education. The second section looks at how communities and NGOs might participate in program planning and implementation. The third section looks at how the ECD program might be managed and supported by local governments and how the central and local governments might interact in this process. The final section looks at the central government's broader role in providing policy guidance and technical support for the national ECD program.

The management processes proposed at the community and local government level are similar to those recommended under the Integrated Approach to Local Development Management (IALDM), which is being advocated as a planning and management mechanism for achieving the overall goals of the Philippine plan of action for children. This approach is summarized in Section J of the supplement volume. Rather than repeat the IALDM strategies here, this chapter attempts to complement and build on them. In particular, it considers the additional staff that would be needed to carry out ECD programs at the local level, recommends specific roles and organizational arrangements for NGO involvement, and proposes a contractual framework for joint ECD program planning and financing by central and local governments.

An ECD Program Model

As noted in Chapter 1, ECD services in health, nutrition, and early education need to vary at different ages to meet the changing needs of the child. Table 4-1 shows a set of core ECD services that correspond to the major child development problems and needs defined in Chapters 1 and 2. Table 4-1 also illustrates the changing nature of the package at different ages. The core package of services is the same as that proposed under the Philippine plan of action for children for meeting the minimum basic needs of children in health, nutrition, and early education.

Although inputs in health, nutrition, and psychosocial development are all important throughout the preschooler's development, the balance between these inputs, and the workload they imply, changes significantly at about the age of 3. During pregnancy and the first three years of life, intensive health and nutrition inputs are needed because during this period the child is most at risk of death or permanent developmental disadvantage from ill health and malnutrition. After age 3, although health and nutrition risks diminish, the workload implications of the psychosocial developmental inputs change significantly. Before age 3, the child's development involves mainly his or her interaction with parents and siblings; after age 3, interaction with groups of other children becomes important for the development of sharing and socialization, and at this age organized early education activities become important.

Service Providers and Their Jobs

One way to respond to the different input and workload requirements at different ages would be to split the primary responsibility for ECD services at the barangay level between two main workers,

Table 4-1. Proposed Services for Early Childhood Development at Different Stages of Life

Stage	Health	Nutrition	Early education

Pregnancy	Immunization against tetanus
	Supplementation with iron
	Prenatal care and instruction
	Identification and referral of high-risk pregnancies
		Arm banding
		Nutrition education
		Supplementation
		  With iodine (ending 1995)
		  With calories[a]
			Education on childcare
			Protecting child from danger
			Encouraging child's attachment with adults
			Providing motor and sensory stimulation

Infancy	Newborn care
	Immunization
	Treatment
	  Of diarrhea
	  Of acute respiratory infection
	Education
	  About malaria
	  About acute respiratory infection
		Education
		  On breastfeeding
		  On weaning
		Growth monitoring and promotion
		Supplementation
		  With vitamin A
		  With iron[a]
		  With calories[a]
			As above

Ages 2–3	In addition to above, parasite control[a]	Growth monitoring and promotion
		Supplementation
		  With vitamin A
		  With iron[a]
		  With calories[a]
			In addition to above, child development
			In thinking skills
			In independence
			In self-control
			In play

Ages 4–6	As above	Growth monitoring and promotion
		Supplementation
		  With vitamin A
		  With iron[a]
			In addition to above, child development
			In fine motor skills
			In language skills
			In cooperation and sharing
			In prewriting and reading skills

a. If required.

one for the pregnant and lactating women and children under age 4 (0 to 36 months old) and one for children ages 4 to 5 (37 months to 60 months old). The primary responsibility for the older age group would be that of the day care worker, who would have special expertise in organized early education. The primary responsibility for the younger age group would be that of the new part-time, paid worker proposed in Chapter 3, who would have special expertise in nutrition. Henceforth, we will refer to this new worker as the child development worker.

A two-worker model is proposed because of the workload, determined by the number of clients in a barangay and the time it would take to deliver services. In a typical barangay of about 1,500 people, the number of children receiving special attention at any one time would be in the range of thirty to fifty for each worker, estimated as follows. For the child development worker, there would be about forty-five pregnant and lactating women at any one time, of whom ten to fifteen might be identified as being at particular nutritional risk by arm banding (measuring the circumference of the upper arm), which is a good indicator of nutritional status. The population of children 6 months to 24 months old would be about sixty-five, of whom up to twenty at a time might be in the supplementation program. For the day care worker, forty children, including the children of the poorest, would be served by the day care center, and a further seven might be served by a home-based center.

The time it would take for the proposed child development worker to provide various services is estimated in Chapter 3. High-quality growth promotion services, including growth monitoring, counseling, and supplementary feeding for the above numbers of children, would probably require four to six hours of work a day, six days a week. Counseling for health and psychosocial development could be integrated into this work and would not therefore require significant additional time. But to this must be added time for coordinating with the field staff of other programs to ensure that integrated interventions (in terms of short-term food subsidy and longer-term livelihood programs) reach food-insecure families. As argued in Chapter 3, it is unlikely that the quality of service, input of time, and accountability required can be expected of volunteers, and for this reason the paid, part-time (six hours a day) position of child development worker is recommended.

To ensure that services are integrated, the job content of the child development worker and of the day care worker should be designed so that each can provide the full range of core health, nutrition, and psychosocial development services appropriate for her age group. Thus, the child development worker would spend most of her time on interventions related to health and nutrition, because these are the priorities for pregnant and lactating women and younger children. But she would also instruct adult family members in how to foster the psychosocial development of children. Dedicating a worker for the 0- to 3-year-olds should enable more emphasis to be given to the psychosocial development of children this age; this age group has gotten insufficient attention from day care workers, who are preoccupied with running preschool activities for older children. The day care worker would spend most of her time on organized early educational activities for groups of children, because this is the primary need of the 4- and 5 year-olds. But the day care worker would also be responsible for responding to the health and nutritional needs of the 4- and 5-year-olds, for example, by providing micronutrient supplements and related nutrition education to parents.

Much more work needs to be done to determine how responsibilities for services and educational tasks should be divided among child development workers, day care workers, and other existing fieldworkers. In outline, the rural health midwife would likely retain responsibility for immunization and for those aspects of prenatal care demanding her higher-level skills. Child development workers and day care workers would likely take the main role in providing other services and interpersonal information, education, and communication (IEC). A key area requiring detailed planning is determining which activities barangay health workers and barangay nutrition scholars would assist with and when and how they would work with the child development workers and day care workers.

Targeting Services

Proposals for targeting child development services on those most at risk were outlined in Chapters 2 and 3. There it was suggested that a survey be used to identify families with pregnant and lactating women or preschool children and to determine which households were particularly disadvantaged. The latter would be determined by an asset measure of poverty and by assessing the nutritional status of pregnant women through arm banding and of children 0 to 6 years old through weighing. This survey would be repeated quarterly and carried out jointly with the community by the child development worker and day care worker. Newly pregnant and lactating women and children 0 to 3 years old would then be assigned to the care of the child development worker, who would enter all the children into the monthly growth-monitoring program, enter qualifying women and children into the feeding program, and enter qualifying families into the nutrition safety net program. Children 4 and 5 years old would be assigned to the care of the day care worker, who would enter qualifying children into the day care center program or the nutrition safety net program, or both.

In addition to the quarterly process for defining priority program clients, it is suggested that a special effort might be made to ensure the convergence of services on the worst-off. This could be done by instituting a "most at risk" list, also updated quarterly, for the five or ten most disadvantaged children in each barangay. The workers carrying out the quarterly survey could jointly draw up this list every month and then meet with their supervisors to jointly propose a combination of interventions, tailored to each family's circumstances. Rural health midwives and social welfare officers would then work with the municipal authorities to ensure that the necessary government support services were made available to the families of these children.

From the point of view of gaining community support for the ECD program, the targeting philosophy most likely to work is one that includes the most disadvantaged but does not exclude all better-off children. Gaining community support is not an issue with the health program because immunization and other activities benefit everyone. The nutrition program is also likely to have widespread benefits, and therefore widespread support, because micronutrient supplementation is required by almost all children and because interventions to counteract protein-energy malnutrition (PEM) also will not be confined to the poorest families. As Chapter 2 noted, PEM is not limited to food-insecure households but also affects improperly weaned children from better-off households. In the case of the preschool program, the price of community support for the program is likely to be the inclusion of some children of the better-off, provided this does not lead to the exclusion of disadvantaged children.

Technical Support and Supervision

As discussed in Chapter 3, infrequent supervision and on-the-job training are believed to be important causes of the low quality of the day care center program. This is related to the fact that the current ratio of supervisors and trainers to barangay-level workers is much less satisfactory in the day care center program than in health and nutrition programs. When the Barangay Day Care Center Law has been fully implemented and there is a day care center in each barangay, there will be twenty to twenty-five day care workers in a typical municipality. But at present staffing levels only one social welfare officer will be available to support them, and she must divide her time between the day care center program and a number of other social welfare activities. This level of staffing contrasts sharply with the situation in health, where there is one rural health midwife for every four or five barangays. Experience from other countries in a variety of outreach programs in health, nutrition, and agricultural extension suggests that it is difficult to achieve good-quality support when the ratio of supervisors to workers is much worse than one to ten. Creating a new municipal-level post for the training and supervision of day care workers is therefore essential. Henceforth, we will refer to workers in this post as early education trainers.

The devolution of program management responsibility to local governments offers an important opportunity to facilitate integrated supervision and technical support to the frontline workers. Where previously rural health midwives and social welfare officers reported up the hierarchy of their respective departments to Manila, now both health and social welfare staff report to the municipal mayor. New training and supervision arrangements will need to be designed to exploit fully the new opportunities for cooperation between social sector field staff.

Field supervision needs to be reoriented so that its primary function is on-the-job training and support rather than inspection. Child development workers and day care workers needing support would be expected to call as needed on the rural health midwife, the social welfare officer, or the early education trainer. For example, where the child development worker thought that a child's persistent malnutrition was disease-related, she would turn to the rural health midwife. Where she thought that it was food security-related, she would turn to the social welfare officer to explore the possibility of livelihood creation opportunities or social safety net support. Or, as another example, where the child development worker needed help with educating parents on the psychosocial developmental needs of a 2-year-old, she would turn to the early education trainer. The potential should be explored for redesigning supervision routines so that on at least some occasions social welfare officers or early education trainers and rural health midwives make joint supervision and training visits to the barangays so as to provide integrated support to the child development workers and day care workers. Both child development workers at the barangay level, together with the social welfare officer/early education trainer and the rural health midwife, should meet fortnightly or monthly to make an integrated assessment of child development problems and progress and to agree on a joint agenda for action.

On-the-job training and support for peripheral workers through supervisory visits also need to be complemented by more formal in-service training. This would best be carried out by an integrated training team consisting of the public health nurse, the nutritionist, the rural health midwives, and the early education trainer, who together have the full range of child development skills. Training curricula should be redesigned in two parts. A common core curriculum covering essential skills in all three subsectors might be taught to the two workers together so as to encourage a consistent, technical, team approach to child development in the barangay. Then each worker would receive more specialized training appropriate for her area of emphasis—the child development worker in food supplementation, for example, and the day care worker in preschool education. The use of training teams should be replicated at the regional level, with appropriate staff from the Department of Health and the Department of Social Welfare and Development nominated to work together in evaluating the results of training in the field, in developing revised training curricula, and in jointly training municipal-level staff as trainers. Considerable further work is needed to develop proposals for an integrated ECD training strategy. As this strategy is developed, it would be important to plan for it to mesh with Department of Interior and Local Government's broader training strategy for strengthening local government: the Integrated Capability Building Program, which is being implemented through the Institute for Local Government Administration.

Experimentation and Evaluation

The service delivery and support structure proposed above is one vision of how integrated ECD services might be organized at the field level. But it is important to experiment with different approaches to delivering services, especially in environments where risks to children are high—in urban slum areas and among indigenous peoples, for example. It is especially important to experiment with different approaches to the delivery, training, and supervision of early education, given that less is known about the relative cost-effectiveness of different approaches in this area than in health and nutrition. To judge which approaches are best requires careful longitudinal evaluations, and this in turn requires strengthening the national capacity to design and manage research and evaluation related to early education in particular but also to ECD as a whole. This institutional strengthening need is discussed further below.

Community and NGO Participation

Official commitment to community and NGO participation in development programs in the Philippines is extremely strong. The Ramos government was elected on a platform of social justice and community empowerment, and community empowerment is a central theme of the medium-term development plan. This plan and the constitution of the Philippines both recognize NGOs as partners of the government in the development process. Despite this strong commitment, there is often confusion when community and NGO participation is discussed, because these terms can be used in different ways. This section therefore first discusses terminology. It then reviews ways in which communities and NGOs are participating in ECD and suggests how their current roles might develop to make services respond better to clients' needs and to give clients more control over services.

How "Community," "NGO," and "Participation" Are Defined

In the Philippines, "community" is most often used in a geographic and administrative sense. Thus, when government officials talk of "the local community," what is generally meant is the geographic community living in the local barangay, and when they talk of "community leaders," what is meant is the barangay council. In this sense, the Philippines has a strong and universal set of community institutions, in which the barangay council contains representatives of different parts of the village and in which different barangays are in turn represented on the municipal council. Devolution has given local councils much more importance because not only municipalities but also barangays have a percentage of revenues allocated to them to spend at their discretion. Community leaders must look both upward and downward: on the one hand, their job is to represent the local community to government at some higher level; on the other hand, and increasingly since devolution, community leaders also are the government in the local area.

In addition to the more than 40,000 barangays and 1,500 municipalities, which are the local communities in the geographic and official sense of the word, there are many more "communities of interest," both within official communities and cutting across them. For example, within barangays are occupational communities, such as fishing and farming families, and income groups, such as landlords and landless laborers, who may feel a stronger sense of community with their peers than with the barangay as a whole. Other communities, such as indigenous communities, may be scattered across several municipalities and interspersed among nonindigenous families but nevertheless feel a strong sense of community. These community groups vary greatly in the degree to which they act as or are represented as community interest groups. For example, indigenous communities may have little or no effective voice in local affairs. And local elites tend to dominate barangay and municipal councils; the degree to which they effectively represent poorer income and occupational interest groups varies widely.

Many community interest groups have formalized themselves as "People's Organizations," officially defined as "bona fide associations of citizens with demonstrated capacity to promote the public interest and with identifiable leadership, membership, and structure." People's Organizations are often registered as NGOs, but they are a distinguishable type of NGO in that they are primarily engaged in representing and helping themselves, whereas most NGOs are set up to help others.

NGOs are defined by the National Economic and Development Authority (NEDA) as "private, nonprofit, voluntary organizations committed to the task of socioeconomic development and established primarily for service." The official definition includes several types of NGOs, such as primary NGOs, which directly provide services; "intermediary" NGOs, which provide financing, training, or technical assistance for other NGOs; advocacy NGOs; and NGO networks, which link NGOs for information exchange or for any of the previous purposes. Here, the definition will also include the for-profit private sector, in the broadest interpretation of the term.

There are many types and degrees of participation, with quite different implications for community empowerment. At the weakest end of the spectrum is consultation with clients, either about program design during the planning stage or program effectiveness during implementation. Financial participation—contributing in cash or kind to a program—is also a weak form of participation, unless it is coupled with increased control over the program in return for contributions. A community role in monitoring program performance is a stronger form of participation, because it implies some say in management. Full community empowerment comes only when communities take over and run an organization or program, as with some agricultural cooperatives, for example. NGOs may also participate in development programs in all these different ways. In addition, because of their expertise, NGOs may be organizers and mobilizers of communities themselves. And they may be trainers, advisors, and consultants to either people's or governmental organizations.

Forms of Participation

CONSULTATION AND INFORMATION GATHERING. Processes for consultation with communities are built into the formal system of local government, from the barangay assemblies at the lowest level to the local health and education boards, which are each mandated to have at least one NGO member, up to the Regional Development Councils, a quarter of whose members must be drawn from NGOs and People's Organizations. But these processes are not focused explicitly on ECD concerns, nor are they necessarily the best channels for consulting the community groups most in need of ECD programs: the processes are formal, the most disadvantaged may not have equal access to them, and local officials may not have the technical skills to elicit the information required. Therefore, just as the central government should set up a systematic process of consultation to find out local governments' priorities and preferences, so should the central and local governments jointly set up a similar process with People's Organizations, NGOs, and communities.

The initial consultations should focus on the level of demand that clients are likely to have for the proposed interventions and the kind of detailed program design that is likely to be most acceptable. As an example of the first, the rapid expansion of the day care center program by local governments indicates strong local demand, but carefully structured consultation could help to determine whether this demand is being expressed by the most disadvantaged, as well as by better-off groups already more convinced of the value of early education. As an example of the second, consultation would help determine the types of supplementary foods that are most locally acceptable, the times of day that are convenient for mothers and children to come for supplementation, and how supplementary feeding can be designed so that it is least likely to substitute for meals children are already getting.

Other important, and more general, questions for exploration with both clients and service providers include the following. Who are the main caregivers for preschoolers and how much time is available for child care? What are the main behavioral practices with regard to child health, nutrition, and early education? What are people's perceptions of the main child development problems affecting their family and barangay? Whom do they see as the people worst affected? What child development services are they aware of in their area? Do they have access to them? How do they rate their performance? What kinds of services do they wish to have? Do they pay for any services, and if so, how much? Would they pay for other interventions, and if so, how much? Do people have a voice in what is now going on in ECD? How could their involvement be increased?

Because of the depth of information required, these consultations would need to be carried out through small-sample focus groups and structured interviewing rather than through large-scale questionnaire surveys. Such consultations might best be contracted to NGOs that have the confidence of communities, the necessary ECD and social research skills, and the independence from government. In addition to carrying out such consultations in "typical" barangays, special care would be needed to stratify the sample so that it included a disproportionate number of communities and families of the types identified in Chapter 2 as being most at risk.

Very little qualitative information of the above kind is currently available. The results of such consultations are essential for developing a "menu" of program options responding to local demand and appropriate for different circumstances. Such consultations should be repeated regularly once a program has begun so that midcourse corrections can be made on the basis of clients' feedback; the service statistics produced by program monitoring systems cannot capture the qualitative dimensions of clients' perceptions.

PERFORMANCE REVIEW BY CLIENTS. Performance monitoring in the ECD program has mostly been designed to keep administrators up the line informed, in keeping with the program's historically centralized, top-down structure. Redesigning the monitoring system so that its primary function is to let local people know how well the program is serving them has great, unexploited potential for community empowerment. Publicly posting a few well-chosen performance indicators at the day care center could stimulate clients' and village leaders' interest and motivate workers. Useful models of community information systems already exist. Examples in the Philippines include the ones developed by the Area-Based Child Survival and Development Program and the Integrated Approach to Local Development Management Program (see, respectively, Sections I and J of the supplement volume). And India has long displayed growth-monitoring information to encourage community participation and motivate workers. It would be useful to synthesize from these and other experiences in community information systems a "best practice" approach to reflecting performance in health, in nutrition, and in early education.

It is suggested that the public posting of performance information be coupled with a redefinition of the function of parents' committees (now often dormant) to become parents' monitoring committees. Currently, these committees meet when called by a day care worker, mainly to extract financial contributions from parents or to provide information and education. It is proposed that the system be reversed: that the parents' committee call the workers to meetings led by parents to review problems and progress with the program. Such a reversal would be an important step toward the eventual goal of community management.

Communities would be empowered and program performance improved if a "verbal autopsy" were done whenever a young child died in the community. In verbal autopsies, community representatives, local service providers, and senior supervisors meet to establish not only the immediate cause of death but also why the program failed to prevent or treat the problem and how a similar outcome can be avoided in the future. Even though focused on child survival rather than development, verbal autopsies could nevertheless powerfully improve communities' understanding and control of the child development program and make workers more accountable to clients.

PLANNING AND MANAGING INTERVENTIONS. Although, as a community empowerment goal, the child development program should routinely consult with clients and involve them in program review, true community management is a more distant goal. Furthermore, it is probably attainable in the near future only for communities that have the support and guidance of an experienced NGO.

A good model for fostering community management with the assistance of an experienced NGO is provided by the Department of Health's Community Health Partnership Program. This program began in 1990 and is now expanding to forty-eight provinces, after good experience in an initial sixteen. Under the program, local NGOs are invited to form partnerships with local governments and People's Organizations to jointly plan and carry out small-scale public health projects. The Department of Health provides planning grants for partnership formation and planning workshops; project grants for implementing the plans; and institutional development grants for improving the capacity of a limited number of NGOs in community mobilization and health development. The funds are managed by one of the NGOs as trustee for the partnership. The program has successfully involved communities in defining their own priorities and building their planning and management experience.

Where appropriate NGOs exist, it is recommended that this approach be broadened to become the main local mechanism for planning and managing child development, with three main changes of emphasis, as follows. First, the program content eligible for financing should be broadened beyond health to include nutrition and early education. Second, the initial focus of the partnership should become the development of an integrated ECD implementation plan that would be negotiated with and partly financed by the central government. The concept of these jointly financed implementation plans for ECD is further developed below in the discussion on program management under devolution. Third, in many areas there would be a need to strengthen the municipal governments' role in the partnerships, which in many cases have been dominated by the NGOs or the provincial governments, or both.

A very large number of nonprofit NGOs are involved in direct service provision. But none of the three main sources of information currently have a good estimate of the numbers involved in ECD. NEDA's NGO directory lists 1,492 NGOs, of which 124 provide services for children. Of these, only thirty-two specify preschool children as their targets. But many NGOs will not have responded to the NEDA survey, and many of the 1,492 listed are involved in multisectoral activities that include ECD, even if this is not specified as the organization's main focus in the directory. NGO records are also kept by the line agencies, although these are limited to the NGOs they have accredited: in 1991, the Department of Social Welfare and Development had accredited only eighty child-caring institutions, and the Department of Health's NGO directory listed only thirty-six NGOs active in health care for the 0–6 age group. The third potential source of information, the main NGO network—the Caucus of Development NGO Networks (CODE-NGO)—keeps no figures on numbers involved in ECD, but the fact that CODE-NGO is itself a coalition of ten NGO networks, one of which is itself a coordinating body for thirty-two sectoral and regional networks, gives some idea of the extent of the NGO movement in the Philippines.

Although the number of NGOs has mushroomed since the Aquino government opened the door to partnership, most of the NGOs involved in ECD are very small, have limited coverage in some of the geographic areas of greatest need, and range widely in the quality of their work, many being more experienced at community mobilization than the technical aspects of ECD. Although the NGO movement clearly has a very significant contribution to make in child development, it is also clear that it is not poised to fill the large gaps in the quality and coverage of services. Therefore, in addition to developing a financing window for NGO involvement in ECD along the lines of the Community Partnerships discussed above, there should be an aggressive program to develop NGOs' capacities in geographic areas where NGOs are currently inactive or active on a small scale and where they have a particular comparative advantage. Most obviously, this program would be in areas where there are indigenous communities, where the program can especially benefit from NGOs' skills in listening; information, education, and communication; and community mobilization.

Hard information about the for-profit sector in ECD is in even shorter supply than for nonprofit NGOs. Given the public's unwillingness and inability to pay for preventive health care and nutrition interventions (see Chapter 5), the commercial sector is most active in preschool education. In 1991 the Department of Education, Culture, and Sports had accredited 1,313 private preschools, and it is believed that there are several times that number of small, nonaccredited preschools and day care centers. The presumption is that most of these schools are in urban areas and cater to the better-off, but a survey is urgently needed to get a better idea of the schools' numbers, regional distribution, fees, clientele in terms of income, and quality. Only then will it be possible to meaningfully review government policy toward the for-profit sector.

The government is adopting a somewhat passive stance in relation to the private sector; its main involvement is accreditation. A more proactive policy toward the private sector would be desirable, beginning with experiments to improve the quality of private sector services by providing technical assistance and training and, more radically, by franchising preschools on a contract basis. However, given that such activities would increase rather than reduce the managerial burden on already stretched government staff, these possible interventions would need to be carefully evaluated for cost-effectiveness, including their hidden costs to government, before being undertaken on a large scale.

PROVIDING SUPPORT SERVICES. The small size of nearly all child development NGOs in the Philippines means that even the best will have relatively little impact as direct service providers. The most cost-effective way for the highest quality NGOs to use their scarce skills may therefore be to leverage them by helping them help other institutions expand and improve the quality of their own services. The government is already drawing on the skills of some NGOs in this way. For example, the Nutrition Center of the Philippines has carried out a wide range of research and experimentation in nutrition, and this has been drawn on by the government. Helen Keller International has assisted the Department of Health and the National Nutrition Council with designing and implementing the micronutrient program. The Community of Learners Foundation is helping the Department of Social Welfare and Development with curriculum development. And Save the Children (U.S.A.) is working with the Department of Social Welfare and Development and local governments to develop a resource center for child development training in the Visayas.

Ways in which NGO skills could be leveraged through contracts with the government might include:

- Providing technical expertise for implementing the proposed systematic consultations with local governments and communities
- Developing curricula for the proposed integrated ECD training for day care workers, child development workers, and their supervisors/trainers
- Training trainers, working with the regional offices of the Department of Health and the Department of Social Welfare and Development
- Experimenting with new approaches to service delivery and helping to evaluate experiments carried out by others
- Helping to develop the institutional capacity of other NGOs operating in underserved, especially disadvantaged areas
- Carrying out policy analysis and evaluation of program activities on contract to the central support institutions (see further below).

Program Management under Devolution

When the Department of Health and the Department of Social Welfare and Development were devolved, beginning in 1991, the consequences for both departments were profound. The Department of Health lost about 40 percent of its budget and more than 45,000 staff members, and the Department of Social Welfare and Development more than half its budget and more than 22,000 social welfare officers and day care workers. The changes were also profound for local governments faced with new responsibilities for program management and with considerable freedom of choice in how to spend the revenues newly allotted to them. This section reviews the changes for both levels of government and suggests directions in which the management of the child development program might evolve in response.

The Local Government Scene

The devolution process was initiated during the last year of the Aquino government but was mainly implemented during 1992 and 1993, in the first years of the Ramos government. Budgets and staff were devolved rapidly during this period, the last central staff being absorbed by local governments in 1993. The speed of the exercise meant that there was little time to train local government managers for their new responsibilities. Nor did mayors have a clear picture in advance of what funds they would receive and when. By mid-1994, the dust was only just beginning to settle. Fairly good information was available about which local governments had benefited and which had lost financially from the devolution, but it was far from clear how the priorities of local governments would evolve over the medium term.

Initial reports from many local governments suggested that the revenue allocations they had received from the center were inadequate to maintain services at predevolution levels. But this perception was belied by a study of devolution in the health sector (World Bank 1994b), which showed that after devolution more than 90 percent of municipalities were in fact as well off as before, if not better off. Nevertheless, the shortage of funds for the social sectors experienced by many local governments was real, a product of the uncoordinated way in which devolution took place. Many local governments received their revenue allocations before learning the details of the social sector staff and activities they would be responsible for absorbing and allocated funds for new infrastructure projects that they later realized were needed to finance existing programs. Tied into infrastructure contracts and obliged to pay the salaries of the staff they had inherited from the national government, many local governments cut back the nonsalary recurrent budget for social programs, sometimes the only funds they had the discretion to cut.

The vast majority of local governments benefited rather than lost from devolution, and the World Bank study (World Bank 1994b) noted that the cities benefited far more than the municipalities. Furthermore, the cities, rather than the poorer rural and urban municipalities, had the better tax base for augmenting devolved revenues with additional resources of their own. Given that the cities were in many cases already better off than the rural areas, devolution may have worsened rather than improved preexisting inequities in the distribution of resources. So although the local governments took on full responsibility for program management, the vast majority of them did not have the financial wherewithal to remedy the deficiencies they inherited in the coverage and quality of social sector services (Chapter 2). In short, outside the cities, local governments that were disadvantaged before devolution remain disadvantaged, and wherever there was a case for central government support before devolution, this case remains valid after devolution. The financial role of the central government in the postdevolution environment is explored further in Chapter 5.

The study on the devolution of the health sector (World Bank 1994b) looked only at the revenue and expenditure balance at the time of devolution. There is very little evidence of how local governments have managed the social sectors since then; remedying the shortage of information in this area is a high priority. From anecdotal information and field visits, the picture appears to be extremely varied. Depending on the priorities of the local mayor and council, some local governments appear to have done more in the social sectors, for example, by rapidly expanding the day care center program. Others have given the social sectors low priority, preferring to spend discretionary funds on roads and other physical infrastructure projects.

Within the social sectors, certain patterns seem to be emerging. In social welfare, as noted in Chapter 3, local governments have given higher priority to establishing new day care centers than to improving the quality of existing ones. And in health, also as noted in Chapter 3, cutbacks in travel allowances and reluctance to send staff for training courses are beginning to reduce the quantity and quality of field supervision and training, and shortages of materials are an increasing cause for concern. The danger is that local governments will respond to public demand for preschool facilities and curative health care, especially in urban areas, at the expense of educational quality and preventive health care, particularly in remoter areas. But too little time has elapsed since devolution, and too little information has been collected, for firm judgments about trends to be made.

The Institutional Role of the Central Government

The Department of Health and the Department of Social Welfare and Development have been gradually adapting to a new role. They no longer manage the programs they formerly ran but nevertheless are expected by the Philippine legislature and the public to set policy and see that national objectives are met. Rather than managing the programs directly, both departments are now learning how to influence the way local governments manage the programs. Using a combination of the three levers now available to them, the departments provide training and technical assistance, market priority programs, and use incremental financing from the center to supplement and influence local government spending. These roles are discussed in turn below.

TRAINING AND TECHNICAL ASSISTANCE. Of the three roles, the provision of training and technical assistance was the most familiar to the departments because it was already a function of their regional offices. The main challenge of the Department of Health's regional offices, which were already strong in most parts of the country, is to complement its existing capacity in technical training with a new capacity for training local governments in health service management. Both the Department of Health and the local governments are making a substantial investment in developing this capacity under the institutional development component of the Department of Health's Women's Health and Safe Motherhood Program. The Department of Social Welfare and Development, however, which was less than a seventh of the Department of Health's size before devolution, will need not just to strengthen but to create a new training support capacity if it is to be able to serve the needs of the fast-growing day care center program.

For both departments, the regional training centers, even when reoriented and expanded, will be too few and far removed to provide for the training needs of more than 1,500 municipalities—an average of one hundred for each region. It will therefore also be important for the regional offices to work with the provincial governors in their areas to develop training support at the provincial level. Given that provincial budgets are limited and that the governors' first priority may be the support of programs for which the provinces are directly responsible (such as the hospital network), central financing to develop the capacity to train at the provincial level will be necessary.

MARKETING AND INFORMATION-GATHERING. Since devolution, local governments can choose how much to invest in the social sectors; which of the social sector programs they will assign priority to; and, within each program, which staff members will be sent for training and how often. If the national government wishes to expand or improve the quality of the child development program, it will first have to successfully advocate that program's importance and then market the specific kinds of interventions it believes will be most effective. The central government has very little experience in this. It does, however, have a cadre of staff with experience in the social marketing of specific health and nutrition interventions to families. With appropriate assistance from private sector marketing experts, these skills in social marketing can be reoriented toward marketing the benefits of investment in child development and other social sector priorities to local governments.

Before a successful marketing effort can be developed, much more information is needed about local governments' behavior, priorities, and levels of understanding with regard to child development. Surveys and focus group consultations will be needed to answer, among others, the following questions. How has social sector spending by local governments changed since devolution? What priority does child development have within social sector spending? Within child development, how much is spent on improving quality and on nonsalary recurrent costs? What do local governments see as the main constraints affecting current child development activities? Do they perceive that there is a child malnutrition problem in their area? Do they perceive that nutrition and preschool activities are of such low quality that much of their benefit is lost? If they had additional money to invest, where would they put it? If offered additional funds by the national government, would they be prepared to complement them with their own, and if so, how much of their own? How fast are local government resources—internally generated and from revenue allotments—likely to grow?

FINANCING CHILD DEVELOPMENT. The market failure and cost-effectiveness rationales for the central government to invest in child development are reviewed in Chapters 1 and 5. This section discusses the managerial issues raised by the continuing need for financing. The central issue is the tension between, on the one hand, the national government's need for consistency and accountability in the implementation of the policies and programs it finances and, on the other hand, the local governments' wish to respond flexibly to locally perceived priorities and needs, the facilitation of which was the main original rationale for devolution.

Of the devolved departments, the Department of Health has made the most progress in developing mechanisms for managing central financial support. The department is conscious of the need to maintain existing public health programs and to avoid central financing being a substitute for local government investment that might otherwise have gone into health. Therefore, the Department of Health, through its regional offices, has negotiated with local governments a series of Comprehensive Health Care Agreements, in which local governments undertake to maintain existing levels of service in the key public health programs as a precondition of continued central financing. Because of the large number of local governments, these agreements have been negotiated with the provinces, and it is the responsibility of the provinces to secure the participation of the municipalities in their area. The Department of Health then plans to enter into a series of additional agreements, annexed to the original agreement and part of it, governing the financing and implementation arrangements for each of the core investment packages set out in its ten-year perspective plan. The first of these is the package for Women's Health and Safe Motherhood. The Department of Health's next priority is an investment package for child development.

The Department of Social Welfare and Development has not yet developed a similar mechanism for local government financing because its resources for augmenting local governments have been limited to a few small-scale projects. But if the Department of Social Welfare and Development is to take a lead role in early education, as proposed here, it would be desirable for the Department of Social Welfare and Development to adopt a similar mechanism and for the Department of Health, the Department of Social Welfare and Development, and the local governments to enter into joint "Child Development Program Agreements" that would integrate all investment in health, nutrition, and early education for preschoolers. These agreements would set out the respective parties' mutual understanding of which activities should have priority during a five- or six-year period; the targets to be achieved during the period; the resources required to reach these targets; and the changing share of central and local government contributions, with a provision for the local government's share to increase progressively with its revenue growth so as to ensure long-term sustainability. Annual action plans and budgets would then be negotiated as the program proceeded, within the framework of the initial overall agreement.

Flexibility in Implementation

Child Development Program Agreements would be advantageous to the central government in fostering consistency and accountability. But they could become straitjackets for local governments and communities unless the agreements avoid standard blueprints and build in flexibility of response to local needs. Three steps should be taken to ensure that they do. First, the central government should offer local governments a menu of options having a differing balance of interventions and implementation arrangements for different risk, geographic, and cultural conditions.

Second, local governments should be encouraged to come up with variations on these options, and the variations should then be appraised by and negotiated with the center. Finally, once implementation begins, negotiation of the annual action plans should be approached flexibly so that the program can be adjusted by mutual agreement in the light of the implementation experience.

Examples of ways in which the menu of options might differ from local government to local government, or barangay to barangay, would include variations in the ratio of child development workers to clients or in the way services are provided. With regard to the former, in certain communities, such as some slum or indigenous communities, the majority of children might be seriously disadvantaged, and in that case it might be necessary to provide double the density of workers and services planned for a typical barangay. Some better-off communities, by contrast, will have too few malnourished children to justify having a new child development worker. And over time, as malnutrition rates fall and private sector preschool services expand, an increasing number of communities will evolve to the point where a single child development worker can manage the program. Differing local conditions may also demand different kinds of services as well as differing worker-client ratios. For example, where communities are scattered, it may be appropriate to develop more small, locally accessible, home-based preschools and rely less on the standard forty-child day care center model. And in urban slum areas, where extended families are not available, more attention will need to be paid to developing full day care in addition to preschool services.

Central Support and Direction

Because of time and budget limitations, the study on which this book is based could neither look at all the support institutions nor do an in-depth analysis of any single one. More work would be required, in consultation with the agencies and their clients in government, to develop detailed recommendations and plans for institutional development. The institutions discussed below are limited to the Council for the Welfare of Children (CWC), which is the national oversight agency for children; the National Nutrition Council (NNC); and the Food and Nutrition Research Institute (FNRI).

The Council for the Welfare of Children

The CWC was founded in 1978 with a mandate to coordinate and implement the enforcement of laws relating to children, formulate national policies and programs for children and monitor and evaluate their implementation, advocate new interventions where appropriate, and mobilize resources for the sector. The CWC is an attached agency of the Department of Social Welfare and Development, with the secretary of the Department of Social Welfare and Development as its chair. The governing board consists of representatives of eight government departments and three private individuals. The board is supported by a technical management committee consisting of the bureau and service heads of the main government agencies dealing with children and of the heads of selected NGOs. The committee operates through five sectoral panels, concerned with health and nutrition; population and social welfare; education; livelihood and shelter; and legal protection and welfare. To support these panels, the CWC has a very small secretariat with thirty-six posts, of which twenty-eight were filled in mid-1994, and a budget of only ₱5 million ($180,000).

A significant accomplishment of the CWC has been the formulation of the Philippine plan of action for children (Chapter 3). It has also been active in formulating regulations for implementing the Child and Youth Welfare Code and the Juvenile Justice System; organizing regional subcommittees for the welfare of children and guidelines for local councils for the protection of children; providing technical assistance in drafting child-related congressional bills; and taking the lead in advocating for children. With assistance from UNICEF, the CWC has also begun to work on a monitoring system for child development interventions, but budget considerations have prevented it from developing this beyond monitoring the limited set of "Mid-Decade Goals" for children to covering the full range of child development activities in health, nutrition, and education.

The CWC's small size, junior staffing levels, and lack of stature in government have inhibited it from effectively analyzing key policy issues and influencing the spending levels of the line agencies that control the resources for children. Staffing issues are compounded by the small size of the CWC's discretionary budget. The CWC is currently obliged to seek resources where it can find them and hence risks having its priorities determined by the objectives of other agencies, domestic or foreign, which have project money to offer. If the CWC is to have credibility and influence with the major actors in government, its structure will need to be reviewed and its budget increased very substantially. Its work program will need to be carefully designed so that it avoids becoming an implementing agency and becomes proficient in policy analysis, coordination, monitoring, research, and evaluation. This suggests that the CWC staff should be relatively small, but high in technical quality and stature so that the institution is well placed to commission, manage, and act on policy and review studies rather than build a new infrastructure to carry out these studies itself.

Legislative action has recently been proposed to convert the CWC to an independent commission; to increase its central staff complement to about sixty professionals, who would work in four divisions—Policy Development, Planning, IEC/Training, and Research; and to create small regional offices with an advisory rather than implementation role. If enacted, this legislation would potentially give the CWC the independence, stature, and technical staff to play an effective role as the apex institution for the ECD program. For this potential to be realized, it will be essential for the key posts in the CWC to be at a high enough level to attract outstanding professionals in the child development field.

The National Nutrition Council

The NNC was founded in 1974 to coordinate the many institutions by then active in nutrition in the Philippines; to provide policy guidance; to carry out monitoring, research, and evaluation; to raise resources; and to promote and pioneer new interventions. The NNC is responsible to a governing board consisting of the secretaries of ten government departments and three private sector groups. This board meets twice a year, often with representation at much lower levels than secretary. The NNC is an attached agency of the Department of Agriculture, to which it reports on a day-to-day basis. The council is supported by a technical committee, headed by the director of the FNRI. The NNC's operational work is conducted by a secretariat, headed by an executive director and made up of three technical divisions: Nutrition Policy and Planning; Nutrition Surveillance; and Nutrition Information and Education. There are also divisions for finance and administration. The staff numbers around 150, about a third of them professionals. The NNC's budget appropriation of about ₱28 million (about $1 million) has remained roughly static over the past ten years and is equaled or outweighed by the support it receives from funding agencies. By far the most important is Japan's four-year commitment of ₱50 million (about $1.8 million) for the LAKASS program (described in Section H of the supplement volume), a second phase of which is being negotiated. Grants for other projects total ₱8 million to ₱10 million (about $400,000).

The most important recent activity of the NNC's Policy and Planning Division has been its lead role in putting together the Philippine Plan of Action for Nutrition, the follow-up plan to the World

Nutrition Conference in Rome in 1992. The Philippine Medium-Term Food and Nutrition Plan, 1993–98, which reflects many of the goals of the World Nutrition Conference and of the Philippine Plan of Action for Children, was approved in principle by the cabinet in 1993, but not with the funding needed to implement it. The NNC has also proposed ten nutrition-related bills to Congress, some at its own initiative and some at the request of legislators seeking technical help in their preparation. Although two have reached the Appropriations Committee, none have become law.

The NNC's difficulties in influencing policy and budget allocation reflect a vicious circle in which some other nutrition councils in Asia also find themselves. The secretariat's advisory role, tiny budget, and lack of political support and access give it little influence over resource allocation decisions in the cabinet or over line agencies with large budgets. The NNC's low government salaries and lack of influence in turn make it difficult to hire the best staff and carry out high-quality policy analysis on issues important to the cabinet and line agencies. Although the NNC has produced many useful pieces of research, its lack of social science skills, among other factors, has meant that it has not fully addressed some critical problems in child nutrition. Among these are the need for a more rigorous analysis of the causes of PEM, the design flaws in the national growth promotion program, and the need to reallocate money assigned to the National Food Authority for food subsidies into more productive interventions.

A fundamental issue is whether the NNC should develop a comparative advantage in one or two major missions or continue with its multiple missions, which include policy analysis and development, program coordination, nutrition surveillance, IEC, and coordination of the implementation of intervention programs. Of all institutions in the Philippines, the NNC has the clearest mandate for nutrition policy analysis, advocacy, and interagency coordination. Careful study is required of the NNC's comparative advantage in nutrition surveillance as against the FNRI's, in IEC for program implementation (as opposed to high-level advocacy) as against the private sector's, and in coordination of the delivery of services as against line agencies having the resources to support local governments on a national scale.

The Food and Nutrition Research Institute

The FNRI started in 1947 as the Institute of Nutrition, a small agency under the Department of Health. It acquired its present name when it was put under the Department of Science and Technology upon that department's creation in 1958. The FNRI's principal mandate is to define nutritional status, which it does through major national surveys every five years, with updates on a smaller set of indicators in between. In addition, it sets technical standards, for example, weight and height standards for anthropometric measurements; develops new food products, such as weaning foods and fortified rice and junk foods; and undertakes research on a wide variety of topics, ranging from overnutrition to food composition and quality to behavioral issues such as breastfeeding. The FNRI's staff numbers about 237, of whom about 150 are professionals. Its budget is about ₱37 million ($1.3 million). An additional third to a half of this amount comes from outside sources, depending on the year.

The FNRI's survey and research work is generally regarded as of high quality. However, a major issue—forced by budget considerations—is the small sample size of the national nutrition surveys, which means that they are valid only at the regional level. As noted in Chapter 2, the aggregated data, which are all that are available (aside from the unreliable Operation Timbang data), make it difficult to target maternal and child nutrition interventions where they are most needed. They are also not useful for program management, because they do not correspond to the administrative units that have become important since devolution. Additional funds to increase the sample size so as to make future national nutrition surveys valid at the provincial level would be well spent. Valid surveys at this level would enable better targeting and more cost-effective use of the much larger sums going into intervention programs. Moreover, by providing local governments and the public with accurate data for the first time, the surveys would act as an incentive for lagging local governments to improve their performance in child nutrition.

Like the NNC, the FNRI is lacking in social scientists, and its research, although useful, has not gone far in addressing the critical issues of causality, management, and cost-effectiveness noted above. How responsibility for this kind of work should be allocated between the FNRI and the NNC is an important issue to resolve. Another is whether the responsible institution, once chosen, should attempt to build up the capacity to do such work in-house, or whether it should contract the work to other agencies that already have some of the technical skills required.

Apex-Level Support for Early Education

Although apex-level support institutions are long established for health and nutrition, early education has no central-level body

Box 4-1. Recommended Structural and Procedural Changes to Foster Integration of Services for Early Childhood Development in the Philippines

Barangay level

- Develop a social marketing program to increase communities' understanding of the concept of integrated ECD.
- Develop an integrated, community-based system and indicators to monitor the performance of the ECD program.
- Revise the job descriptions of ECD workers to ensure integrated attention to health, nutrition, and early education.
- Develop work routines that allocate task responsibilities among full-time ECD workers and volunteer workers (barangay health workers and nutrition scholars).
- Develop joint in-service training programs for field staff.

Municipal level

- Develop a social marketing program to increase local governments' understanding of the concept of integrated ECD.
- Develop an integrated system to monitor the performance of ECD programs at the local government level.
- Revise the job descriptions of ECD supervisors to ensure they provide technical support to all field-level workers, rather than only to the "health" or "social welfare" cadre.
- Develop joint in-service training programs for ECD supervisors.

Provincial and regional levels

- Develop an integrated system to monitor the performance of the ECD program.
- Develop joint training programs for trainers of ECD trainers.

Central level

- Seek support from the Social Development Committee to pursue the vision of an integrated national ECD program.
- Strengthen working-level contacts between the line agencies responsible for ECD.
- Develop an integrated national investment program for ECD.
- Strengthen the Council for the Welfare of Children as the national apex institution for ECD.

giving it the same kind of support in advocacy, policy development, advice-giving, standards development, monitoring, operations research, and evaluation. An issue for government policymakers to consider is whether this kind of institutional support—which will be essential for improving the quality of early education in the Philippines—should be developed by creating an entirely new government institution. In a climate of fiscal concern and civil service streamlining, such an option should be avoided if effective alternatives can be found. Given that technical expertise in early education is more abundant in nongovernmental than in governmental organizations, a cost-effective alternative may be to create a network of governmental and nongovernmental organizations with expertise in these areas as a support system for early education. Such a network would need guidance and coordination from a small secretariat, which in turn would need discretionary budget funds to enable it to commission policy, operations research, evaluation, and other studies from qualified network members. If the network rather than a new institution were created, it would be necessary to agree on an appropriate institutional home for the proposed secretariat.

Conclusions

It is possible to develop an integrated national ECD program that builds on existing interventions, but it will require significant

---

Box 4-2. Proposed Investments to Strengthen Institutional Capacity at Various Levels for Early Childhood Development Programs in the Philippines

- Barangay level: create a new position of child development worker for children under 4.
- Municipal level: create a new position of early education trainer.
- Provincial and regional levels: strengthen the capacity to provide training and support for municipal ECD programs.
- Central level: strengthen the Council for the Welfare of Children as the apex institution for the ECD program.

change in two directions: first, change in institutional process and structure to ensure that existing services are integrated and, second, policy development, additional staff, supervision, and training to ensure manageable workloads and good quality. Both sets of changes would have to be endorsed in principle by the Social Development Committee before a detailed national ECD investment plan is worked out.

Box 4-1 summarizes the structural and procedural changes that are recommended at different levels of the system to foster integration.

Box 4-2 lists the main points in the system where significant investments must be made to ensure good-quality services and good-quality technical and supervisory support. The costs of these investments in institutional capacity are calculated in Chapter 5, as are the costs of noninstitutional inputs, such as civil works, equipment, and supplies, which are also required to strengthen and expand the ECD program.

5. Financing Early Childhood Development

What are the trends and levels of public sector spending on early childhood development (ECD) in the Philippines and how does the spending compare with what other Asian countries spend? How much additional money will be needed to improve the quality and coverage of ECD services so as to meet national goals over the next six years? Where might the money for strengthening and expanding the ECD program in the short term—and sustaining it in the long term—come from? These are some of the questions that will be dealt with in this chapter.

Trends and Levels in Spending

Social Sector Expenditure

Manasan and Llanto (1994) have summarized trends in social sector spending in the Philippines during the 1980s and early 1990s. Social sector spending rose significantly after 1986, with the ending of the economic crisis of the mid-1980s and the coming into power of the Aquino government, which was committed to the poor. From 3.2 percent of gross national product (GNP) during 1975–85, social sector expenditure rose to 4.1 percent of GNP during 1986–93. Social sector spending also rose significantly as a proportion of government spending net of debt service, rising from 24 percent during 1983–85 to 30.1 percent during 1986–93. However, squeezed by increased spending to service debt, the social allocation ratio— social sector spending as a proportion of all government spending— rose more modestly, from 16.7 percent during 1983–85 to 18.5 percent during 1986–93. Debt service has emerged as the main component of government spending, making up 38 percent of the budget during 1986–93 as against 8.3 percent during 1975–82. To have increased the share of social sector spending during this

Figure 5-1. Social Allocation Ratio, Selected Asian Countries, 1988

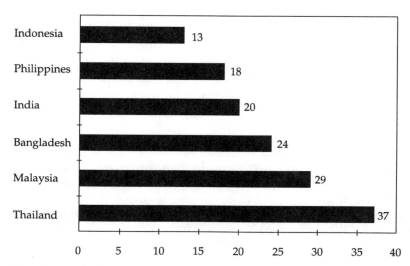

Note: The social allocation ratio is social sector spending as a percentage of all government spending.

Source: Manasan and Llanto (1994).

period, when total government spending net of debt service shrank, is an achievement. Nevertheless, this achievement has to be seen in perspective. At 20 percent in 1993, the social allocation ratio no more than returned to its 1975–82 level, comparing unfavorably with that of several Asian countries (Figure 5-1).

Within social sector expenditure, education has the largest share at 63 percent (Figure 5-2). But because the education budget is almost entirely spent on schoolchildren, it is health expenditure, with only 16 percent of the share, that has the greatest impact on preschoolers. During the economic crisis of 1983–85, spending on education and health fell to about 6.0 percent and 0.5 percent of GNP, respectively. The drop in health spending was sharper than in education—a 40 percent fall in health as against a 10 percent fall in education spending as a proportion of GNP. Spending on education recovered to 13 percent of GNP in 1991 and 10.6 percent of GNP in 1993, but spending on health rose only to 1.0 percent of GNP in 1990 and then fell back to 0.5 percent again in 1993. This level compares poorly with levels in several other Asian countries (Figure 5-3).

Real public spending on health per capita in 1990 was less than 10 percent greater than it was in 1983, just before the economic crisis. The World Development Report *Investing in Health* (World

Figure 5-2. Sectoral Shares of Social Spending in the Philippines, 1991

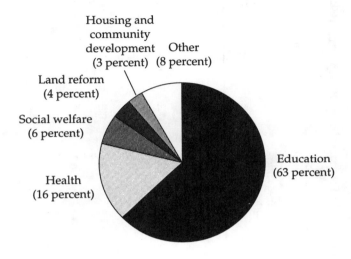

Source: World Bank (1993a).

Figure 5-3. Health Spending as a Percentage of GNP, Selected Asian Countries, Average for 1980–89

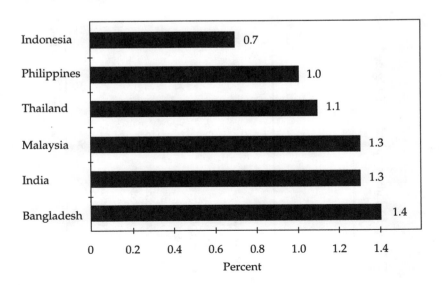

Source: World Bank (1994b).

Table 5-1. Public Spending Budgeted for Key Early Childhood Health Programs in the Philippines, 1994
(millions of pesos)

Program	Department of Health	Local government	United Nations Children's Fund	U.S. Agency for International Development	World Health Organization	Philippine Health Development Project	Canadian International Development Agency	Rotary Club	Australian International Development Assistance Bureau	Urban Health and Nutrition Project	Total
Expanded Program on Immunization	399.3	119.7	13.3	13.7	1.9	0.0	27.4	34.2	6.8	0.0	616.3
Control of diarrheal diseases	47.4	29.9	4.4	3.4	0.6	0.0	0.0	0.0	0.0	0.0	85.7
Control of acute respiratory infections	53.7	18.5	4.8	8.8	1.3	9.0	0.0	0.0	0.0	2.9	98.9
Control of infectious diseases	12.6	0.0	0.0	0.0	0.0	0.0	0.0	0.0	0.0	0.0	12.6
Disease surveillance	62.0	0.0	0.0	4.8	0.0	0.0	0.0	0.0	0.0	0.0	66.8
Total	575.0	168.1	22.5	30.8	3.7	9.0	27.4	34.2	6.8	2.9	880.3

Source: World Bank and ADB data. See Section K of the supplement volume.

Bank 1993b) estimated that the cost of a minimum package of public health and clinical services (that is, excluding hospital care) would be about $12 per head for a typical low-income country. In 1990, just before devolution, total public sector spending on health in the Philippines was about ₱115, or about $4.10 per head (World Bank 1993b), of which less than a quarter went to preventive care.

Expenditure on Early Childhood Development

It is impossible to make an estimate of total spending on ECD in the Philippines because of the lack of data about private sector spending. We can therefore estimate only an order of magnitude of public sector spending.

The main spending affecting preschoolers is on immunization and the programs to control diarrheal diseases and acute respiratory infections. The budgets for each of the three programs in 1994, together with the relevant sources of financing, are given in Table 5-1. Total spending was ₱880 million ($31.4 million), of which the immunization program absorbed 70 percent.

Table 5-2 sets out 1994 budgets for nutrition, totaling ₱854 million ($30.5 million). It leaves out the National Food Authority's spending on the consumer subsidy, because this is not aimed at children, nor does it appear to benefit them significantly (Chapter 3). Spending on child nutrition is probably overestimated, because the "Other programs" category includes some expenditures not aimed solely at children. Table 5-2 illustrates the nutrition program's extreme dependence on PL 480 resources, which made up more than half the program budget in 1994. As noted in Chapter 3, the proposed phaseout of PL 480 support will necessitate a radical reappraisal of the program.

Table 5-3 summarizes the budget for early education in 1994, totaling ₱373 million ($13.3 million). These figures are particularly uncertain. On the one hand, they may overestimate normal spending levels, because the 1994 budget included a ₱95.2 million ($3.4 million) congressional insertion of money from the countrywide development fund, which may not be repeated in later years. On the other hand, many local governments have been rapidly expanding their day care center networks since devolution, although what they have been spending is unknown. The ₱169 million ($6 million) shown for local government spending on the day care center program in 1994 in the table includes only what was devolved to them for this program.

Table 5-2. Public Spending Budgeted for Early Childhood Nutrition in the Philippines, 1994

Source of financing	Millions of pesos
Department of Health's budget	86.1
Foreign assistance to the Department of Health	34.0
Devolved personnel from the Department of Health	162.0
Supplementary feeding program of the Department of Social Welfare and Development	6.8
Supplementary feeding programs of local governments	52.5
PL 480	431.2
World Food Programme	75.5
Other programs	5.8
Total	853.9

Source: World Bank and ADB data. See Section K of the supplement volume.

Table 5-3. Public Spending Budgeted for Early Education in the Philippines, 1994

Source of financing	Millions of pesos
Congressional insertion	95.2
Local government spending on day care program	169.0
Preschool program of Department of Education, Culture, and Sports	100.0
United Nations Children's Fund	8.9
Total	373.1

Source: World Bank and ADB data. See Section K of the supplement volume.

A very rough estimate of planned spending on early childhood development in 1994 is therefore ₱2,107 million (about $75 million), or about $7.80 for each preschooler. This figure would fall to ₱1,581 million (about $56 million), or about $5.90 a head with the phasing out of the PL 480 program and if the apparently exceptional 1994 congressional insertion for early education is not repeated.

Conclusions

In relation to some other Asian countries, the Philippines is under-spending on social sector development. Spending on preschool children gets only a small share of the low overall allocation to the social sectors. Of spending on health, less than 10 percent goes for programs primarily aimed at preschoolers, despite the fact that these are the programs that will have the greatest impact on death and disease rates, given the epidemiology of the Philippines. Spending on child nutrition, a crucial area because of the very high levels of both micronutrient and protein-energy malnutrition (PEM), is dwarfed by the unproductive spending on consumer food subsidies. Public spending on early education is about 40 percent of spending on child health, consistent with the very low coverage of the early education program. Low spending on early childhood development is a matter of great human concern because of the poor developmental situation of young children as measured by several indicators (Chapter 2). It is also a matter of great economic concern because of the important role that investment in human resources has played in the success of the high-growth "East Asian miracle" countries.

There are few signs of positive change in the above situation; in fact, there are some signs that things will get worse. In health, although spending as a proportion of GNP began to recover after the economic crisis of the mid-1980s, this ratio fell again after 1991 and is now back where it was then. In nutrition, spending may fall by nearly half as PL 480 support phases out. In early education, the situation is uncertain; if the 1994 congressional insertion is not repeated, spending may also fall in that subsector.

It is difficult to quantify how far away the Philippines is from what it "should" be spending on child development, because there are no generally accepted norms for this. One estimate (Selowsky 1981) suggests that low-income developing countries should spend 1.4 to 2.2 percent of GNP on this sector. On that basis, and assuming, overoptimistically, that the private sector would provide half the financing, the government should be spending about five times as much on ECD as it does now. But the best way to arrive at an estimate of spending requirements is to build them up from the unit costs and quantities needed to reach desired levels of coverage and quality. The next section attempts to do this.

Six-Year Financing Needs

Here we estimate the investment needed by 2000 to achieve the nation's child development goals. The strategies costed in health, nutrition, and early education are those recommended in previous chapters.

Strategies and Assumptions

The health strategy costed includes, first, the consolidation and expansion of a set of well-established national core programs, including the Expanded Program on Immunization (EPI), control of diarrheal diseases, and control of acute respiratory infections. The main capital replacement cost would be for the EPI cold chain. Second, costing includes interventions for schistosomiasis, malaria, and helminth control in provinces where these are important contributors to child death and disease, and includes national strengthening of the disease sentinel surveillance system. Third, it is assumed that the midwife cadre will expand at a rate in line with population growth.

In nutrition, the core intervention costed is the development of a national program for growth monitoring and promotion, including short-term supplementary feeding of selected children and pregnant women, and interventions to eliminate vitamin A and iodine deficiency and to reduce iron deficiency. The nutrition costing includes the cost of adding a child development worker in each barangay, as proposed above, although this worker would assist with health and early education as well as nutrition interventions (Chapter 4). Finally, costs for information, education, and communication (IEC); training; and monitoring and evaluation are included.

In early education, the main strategies costed are the strengthening of the existing day care centers through the provision of improved materials, training, and supervision, including the creation of a new early education trainer post in each municipality (Chapter 4); the establishment of a day care center in poor barangays not now covered by the program; and the establishment of a demonstration "satellite" home-based day care center in each barangay. For each of the above areas, further details of the costing assumptions are given below and in Section K of the supplement volume.

Because of the many uncertainties involved in the costing, the estimates represent no more than a rough order of magnitude. Among the uncertainties that might affect costs significantly, four stand out. First, policymakers in the central government may opt for different assumptions than those made below about interventions and program phasing. Second, now that devolution has taken place, the types of child development programs that are implemented, and the pace at which they expand, will be determined by local, not central, government. Without widespread consultation with local governments, it is impossible to know whether the type, scale, and pace of investment contemplated below will prove to be realistic. Third, as noted in Chapter 4, the program design will vary significantly in different areas, both in the ratios of staff and other inputs to clients and in the way services are delivered. Order-of-magnitude costing must inevitably be based on standard program inputs to a standard, "typical" barangay, whereas in practice, local conditions, project inputs, and project costs will vary. Finally, the brief study on which this book is based did not allow for a full-scale costing exercise. Many of the unit costs and quantities assumed below would need to be revised when specific investment proposals are prepared. To allow the reader to recalculate costs using alternative assumptions, Section K of the supplement volume contains details of all unit costs and quantities. All costs are in 1994 prices, with no allowance for inflation.

Finally, the investment requirements for ECD are presented in the form of financing gaps between resources currently available and resources required. A distinction is drawn below between the overall financing gap, which would be filled by a mixture of central and local financing, and what might be termed the "magna carta" financing gap.[1] The latter represents the difference between what local governments are theoretically obligated to pay (from the start of 1995) for a recently negotiated, so-called magna carta benefit package for health fieldworkers and what the local governments are able to pay. The distinction is important on two counts. First, these benefits may or may not be continued by local governments, depending on their ability to pay; therefore, it is of interest to show their order of magnitude separately. Second, the benefits are the only costs among the incremental investment requirements that are clearly the obligation of local rather than central government. A cost-sharing policy between central and local government—discussed under Sourcing below—will need to be set up for the remaining, and far larger, portion of the financing gap. For this reason also, it is important to distinguish between the two elements of the overall gap.

Financing Needed for Health

Of the three child development subsectors, the costs for health are probably least controversial. This is partly because the main intervention programs are in place and following appropriate strategies (Chapter 3); the investment requirements are more for building on and consolidating existing plans than for funding changes in strategy. It is also because a major exercise, documented in Alano and others (1993), was recently undertaken by the Department of Health and UNICEF to calculate the costs of reaching the

Table 5-4. Health Program: Estimated Costs, Resources Available, and Financing Gap, Philippines, 1994–99
(millions of pesos)

	1994	1995	1996	1997	1998	1999	Total
Expanded Program on Immunization	312.8	362.1	437.6	479.5	502.0	469.5	2,563.4
Control of acute respiratory infections	98.9	104.7	101.1	96.9	95.6	99.5	596.7
Control of diarrheal diseases	109.8	106.4	94.0	93.6	94.8	96.2	594.7
Polio[a]	213.9	210.1	120.0	122.3	124.8	127.3	918.4
Neonatal tetanus[a]	240.1	239.8	213.9	215.5	217.1	218.1	1,344.5
Measles[a]	132.3	129.6	88.5	90.5	92.6	94.7	628.2
Infectious diseases	26.5	26.5	26.5	26.5	26.5	26.5	158.7
Disease surveillance	228.1	54.1	53.5	52.0	52.0	53.5	493.2
Joint cost savings	−36.0	−33.9	−26.9	−24.5	−24.9	−23.6	−169.9
Total resources required	1,326.3	1,199.3	1,108.0	1,152.3	1,180.5	1,161.6	7,128.0
Available resources	880.3	742.9	699.4	701.3	708.1	700.7	4,432.6
Financing gap	445.9	456.4	408.7	451.0	472.4	460.9	2,695.3
Magna carta gap[b]	0.0	147.8	151.2	154.6	158.2	161.8	773.6
Remaining gap	445.9	308.7	257.5	296.4	314.2	299.0	1,921.8

a. The additional costs to meet the reduction and eradication goals are shown here separately from the routine costs for the Expanded Program on Immunization.

b. The difference between what local governments are theoretically obligated to pay (from the start of 1995) for a recently negotiated, so-called magna carta, benefit package for fieldworkers and what the local governments are able to pay; the central government has no obligation to help meet this gap.

Source: World Bank and ABD data. See Section K of the supplement volume.

nation's mid-decade health goals. The costs assumed below for health essentially take the unit costs and quantities from this study and extrapolate them, taking into account changes in population size.

Table 5-4 shows estimates of investment requirements in child health. This estimate diverges from the costings in the Alano study in three significant ways. First, an allowance is made for investment in schistosomiasis, malaria, and helminth control programs in the ten provinces where these are most likely to affect child health. Second, costs are included for expanding and improving the disease surveillance program (see Chapter 2). Third, a reduction has been made for joint cost savings for items such as training, IEC, and monitoring and evaluation, where improvements in one system can serve the needs of several child health intervention programs. The estimates of resources that will be available reflect intentions of Department of Health program managers and the local offices of the main aid donors in 1994. Based on the above assumptions, the financing gap in child health is ₱2,695 million (about $96.3 million) over six years. This includes a magna carta gap of ₱774 million (about $27.6 million) and a remaining gap of ₱1,922 million (about $68.6 million).

Financing Needed for Nutrition

Cost estimates for the micronutrient program were included in the Alano study, and these are used as the basis for the micronutrient program costs here. The main departure is to assume higher levels of achieved coverage—90 percent for women and children, rather than the 65 to 80 percent range adopted in the Alano study. This assumption reflects the high priority given in this book to attacking micronutrient deficiencies, because of both the severity of the problem in the Philippines and the extraordinarily high cost-benefit ratio of investment in this area. As with the estimates for child health, joint cost savings have been assumed for training, IEC, and monitoring and evaluation.

Because the PEM control program needs substantial restructuring (Chapter 3), the program has been completely recosted on the basis of inputs of successful growth promotion programs elsewhere. The major costing assumptions are therefore enumerated here in more detail. *Program coverage* has been assumed to be all rural barangays plus half the urban population (in practice, as noted in Chapter 4, some rural barangays may not require a new PEM control program, whereas barangays that are especially disadvantaged may require double the average resources of staff and other inputs). An *allowance* of P700 (about $25) a month has been assumed for the proposed new child development worker as being the minimum incentive required for good-quality work four to six hours a day. *Lump sum costs* of P84 million (about $3 million) each have been assumed for the monitoring and evaluation and IEC inputs. It has been assumed that the *phasing of implementation* of the revamped PEM program would be over a six-year period, with an additional sixth of the target population covered each year. This relatively slow phasing reflects the substantial reorientation that appears to be required in the PEM program.

For *supplementary feeding*, it has been assumed that children 6 months to 24 months old who are eligible for feeding would receive a 400-calorie supplement six days a week for three months. However, the cost of supplementary feeding for children is difficult to calculate because of uncertainties about the cost for a ration of food and the percentage of the target population who would be fed each year. The former is uncertain because the cost of a ration in current feeding programs in the Philippines, P2.40 (about $0.09), seems high by international standards. The latter is uncertain because both the number of growth-faltering children and the rate at which malnutrition will fall are unknown. Table 5-5, therefore, presents a sensitivity analysis of the annual cost of supplementing the diets of 385,000 children—the number of children of target age who would come into the program each year, assuming that implementation would expand evenly over six years.

Table 5-6 shows cost estimates for the nutrition program, using a low estimate for supplementary food. For this table, it is assumed that the cost of an appropriate weaning food can be reduced to P2 (about $0.07) for each child-ration and that no more than 18 percent of the children would be in the supplementation program at any time. Supplementation costs for children would then be P924

Table 5-5. Sensitivity Analysis of the Cost of Supplementary Food per 385,000 Children in the Philippines
(millions of pesos)

Percentage of children fed	At P1.4 per ration	At P2.0 per ration	At P2.4 per ration
18	30	43	52
25	42	60	72
33	55	79	95

Source: World Bank and ADB data. See Section K of the supplement volume.

Table 5-6. Nutrition Program: Estimated Costs (Low Estimate), Resources, and Financing Gap, Philippines, 1994–99
(millions of pesos)

	1994	1995	1996	1997	1998	1999	Total
Micronutrient supplementation	503.4	514.8	525.7	537.4	549.3	561.5	3,192.2
PEM control							
Equipment	10.0	10.0	10.0	10.0	10.0	10.0	60.0
Allowances for child development workers	46.9	93.8	140.8	187.7	234.6	281.5	985.4
Supplementary food	78.1	156.3	234.4	312.6	390.7	468.8	1,640.9
Training, IEC, monitoring and evaluation	51.5	51.5	51.5	51.5	51.5	51.5	308.8
Total resources required	690.0	826.4	962.4	1,099.1	1,236.1	1,373.3	6,187.3
Available resources	853.9	447.9	413.1	427.1	444.2	364.8	2,951.0
Financing gap	0.0	378.5	549.3	672.0	791.9	1,008.6	3,400.3
Magna carta gap[a]	0.0	75.0	77.0	79.0	80.0	82.0	393.0
Remaining gap	0.0	303.5	472.3	593.0	711.9	926.6	3,007.3

Note: Low estimate: supplementary food costs are calculated at ₱2 (about $0.07) for each child-ration, with supplements being received by, on average, 18 percent of the children and 25 percent of pregnant women. PEM is protein-energy malnutrition; IEC is information, education, and communication.
a. See the note to Table 5-4.
Source: World Bank and ADB data. See Section K of the supplement volume.

Table 5-7. Nutrition Program: Estimated Costs (High Estimate), Resources, and Financing Gap, Philippines, 1994–99
(*millions of pesos*)

	1994	1995	1996	1997	1998	1999	Total
Micronutrient supplementation	503.4	514.8	525.7	537.4	549.3	561.5	3,192.2
PEM control							
Equipment	10.0	10.0	10.0	10.0	10.0	10.0	60.0
Allowances for child development workers	46.9	93.8	140.8	187.7	234.6	281.5	985.4
Supplementary food	122.3	244.6	366.9	489.2	611.5	733.8	2,568.4
Training, IEC, monitoring and evaluation	51.5	51.5	51.5	51.5	51.5	51.5	308.8
Total resources required	734.1	914.7	1,094.9	1,275.8	1,456.9	1,638.3	7,114.7
Available resources	853.9	447.9	413.1	427.1	444.2	364.8	2,951.0
Financing gap	0.0	466.8	681.8	848.7	1,012.7	1,273.6	4,283.6
Magna carta gap[a]	0.0	75.0	77.0	79.0	80.0	82.0	393.0
Remaining gap	0.0	391.8	604.8	769.7	932.7	1,191.6	3,890.6

Note: High estimate: supplementary food costs are calculated at ₱2.40 (about $0.09) for each child-ration, with supplements being received by, on average, 25 percent of the children and 30 percent of pregnant women. PEM is protein-energy malnutrition; IEC is information, education, and communication.

a. See the note to Table 5-4.

Source: World Bank and ADB data. See Section K of the supplement volume.

million ($33 million) over six years. Furthermore, it is assumed that 25 percent of pregnant women would receive a 600-calorie supplement six days a week for six months to ensure coverage of women likely to have a baby with a low birth weight. Supplementation costs for pregnant women for six years would then be about ₱714 million ($25.5 million). Total supplementary food costs for children and pregnant women would be about ₱1,640 million ($58.6 million). In this scenario, the rough order of magnitude of the investment financing gap in nutrition is ₱3,400 million (about $121 million), including a magna carta gap of ₱393 million (about $14 million).

Table 5-7 uses a high estimate for supplementary food costs. (Later tables use nutrition program costs that are an average of the low and high estimates.) For the high estimate, it is assumed that food costs would be ₱2.40 (about $0.09) for each child-ration (about the cost of supplementary feeding in the Catholic Relief Service program today) and that 25 percent of children on average would be in the supplementation program. Supplementation costs for children would then be ₱1,530 million (about $55 million) over six years. It is also assumed that 30 percent of pregnant women would be supplemented at the higher unit cost of food, in which case the supplementation cost for women would be ₱1,030 million (about $37 million). In this scenario, the rough order of magnitude of the investment financing gap in nutrition is ₱4,283.6 million (about $153 million), of which ₱393 million ($14 million) is the magna carta financing gap. In both scenarios, the costs of the food supplementation program continue to rise over the six-year period, reflecting continuing program expansion. From year seven onward, supplementation costs would likely fall as the program reached full geographic coverage and malnutrition rates declined.

Financing Needed for Early Education

The inputs envisaged for early education divide into two types: those for improving the quality of the existing day care center system, and those for expanding its coverage. Costing for improving quality is based on six main assumptions. First, 30 percent of the existing day care centers would require an investment of an average of ₱2,000 (about $71) to make them safe for children. Second, existing day care workers would receive reorientation training at the beginning of the program and refresher training three years later. Third, the allowances of existing day care workers would be topped up by an average of ₱300 (about $11) each month to ₱800 (about $29) each month to reflect a minimum incentive for a full-time job. Fourth, a new position of early education trainer would

Table 5-8. Early Education Program: Estimated Costs, Resources, and Financing Gap, Philippines, 1994–99
(millions of pesos)

	1994	1995	1996	1997	1998	1999	Total
Existing system							
Allowances for day care workers	123.0	123.0	123.0	123.0	123.0	123.0	738.0
Salaries of social welfare officers	46.0	46.0	46.0	46.0	46.0	46.0	275.7
Subtotal	169.0	169.0	169.0	169.0	169.0	169.0	1,013.7
Improvements in quality							
Rehabilitation of day care centers	6.2	6.2	0.0	0.0	0.0	0.0	12.3
Strengthening of training institutions	5.4	4.6	4.6	4.6	4.6	4.6	28.4
Training of social welfare officers and early education trainers	8.0	0.0	0.0	5.8	0.0	0.0	13.8
Training of day care workers	16.0	0.0	0.0	6.7	0.0	0.0	22.7
Salaries of new early education trainers	91.9	91.9	91.9	91.9	91.9	91.9	551.5
Topping up of allowances for additional day care workers	73.8	73.8	73.8	73.8	73.8	73.8	442.8
Learning materials and maintenance	81.7	20.1	20.0	81.7	20.0	20.0	243.7
Parent effectiveness materials	0.3	0.3	0.3	0.3	0.3	0.3	1.8
Subtotal	283.2	196.9	190.7	264.8	190.7	190.7	1,317.0
System expansion							
Day care centers							
Construction, furnishings, and materials	197.9	197.9	197.9	197.9	197.9	197.9	1,187.6
Allowances for new day care workers	21.1	42.3	63.4	84.6	105.7	126.9	444.0
Training of new day care workers	1.7	1.7	1.7	3.1	3.1	3.1	14.6
Teaching supplies and maintenance	11.0	21.9	32.9	43.9	54.8	65.8	230.3
Home-based centers							
Home upgrading	0.0	33.7	33.7	33.7	33.7	33.7	168.6
Allowances	0.0	32.4	64.7	97.1	129.5	161.8	485.5
Training	0.0	5.3	5.3	5.3	8.9	8.9	33.6
Start-up materials	0.0	5.1	5.1	5.1	5.1	5.1	25.3
Recurrent materials	0.0	0.0	1.7	3.3	5.0	6.6	16.5
Subtotal	231.8	340.3	406.4	474.0	543.8	609.9	2,606.1
Total resources required	683.9	706.1	766.1	907.7	903.4	969.5	4,936.8
Available resources	373.1	218.8	214.2	215.1	214.9	214.9	1,451.0
Financing gap	310.9	487.3	551.8	692.6	688.5	754.6	3,485.8

Source: World Bank and ADB data. See Section K of the supplement volume.

be created and filled in each municipality. Fifth, learning materials and an allowance for building maintenance would be provided at each of the 20,500 existing day care centers. Sixth, training institutions would need to be strengthened (but because the strategy for doing this is unclear, provision is made for this through a lump sum).

Costing for the expansion of coverage assumes the following. First, as with the nutrition program, the coverage target would be all rural barangays plus half the urban population, and on this basis, 13,215 new day care centers would be established, together with the provision of a day care worker, furniture, materials, and an allowance for building maintenance. Second, the cost of building and furnishing a day care center would be only ₱89,800 (about $1,395), because designs based on local materials would be used. Third, one satellite (home-based) center would be established in each of the 33,715 targeted barangays, requiring costing for a worker, materials, and training. (Again, as noted in Chapter 4, the ratio of day care centers to home-based centers may not be one to one, but would vary, depending on local settlement patterns and needs.) Fourth, the allowance for the home-based worker would be ₱400 (about $14) each month, reflecting the lesser hours and responsibility for this work. Fifth, ₱5,000 (about $178) would be provided for the repair and remodeling of homes to make them suitable for preschool and day care purposes. Sixth, the new day care centers would be phased in evenly over a six-year period, and the home-based centers over a five-year period beginning a year later. (The delay would give time to improve the quality of existing day care centers before home-based centers are added to the system.) Details of all these assumptions are given in Section K of the supplement volume.

Table 5-8 summarizes the investments required to improve the quality and coverage of early education. On the basis of an even phasing in of new centers over six years, the order of magnitude of the investment financing gap is about ₱3,490 million (about $124 million).

Conclusion

Based on the above assumptions, the cost over a six-year period of meeting the financing gap to bring the national ECD program up to a level of quality and coverage sufficient to meet national targets would be ₱9.6 billion to ₱10.5 billion ($342 million to $374 million). If the cost is a middle-of-the-range figure of ₱10 billion (about $35.8 million), then ₱1.12 billion (about $40 million) would be the magna carta gap and ₱8.88 billion (about $317 million) the remaining gap, to be filled by a mix of local, central, and foreign aid financing. Table 5-9 shows the breakdown of these costs by subsector, assuming investment in the middle of the range. It indicates that, overall, the resources currently planned for ECD are about 47 percent of needs. But the percentage shortfall is least in the health subsector, which has the most mature program, and is ·substantial both in the nutrition sector, after the withdrawal of PL 480 assistance, and in early education, reflecting the limited resources that have gone into the Department of Social Welfare and Development. About 38 percent of the gap is in nutrition, about 35 percent in early education, and about 27 percent in health.

The above cost estimates are conservative in at least two ways. First, they assume, for simplicity's sake, an even phasing of investment over six years in both PEM control and early education. In practice, it is likely that the phasing of investment may be significantly slower at the beginning, to allow time for pilot testing of the integrated package of activities under the new circumstances of devolution. But it is also possible that, with successful pilot experience, the expansion phase thereafter could be more rapid. If so, the build-up of costs would be faster and the total program costs correspondingly greater. It would be useful to carry out a sensitivity analysis using different phasing assumptions, based on government guidance on its intentions for the program. For the PEM program, it has been assumed that supplementation would be limited to eligible children 6 months to 24 months old; a case could also be made for widening this to children 6 months to 36 months old, which would substantially increase costs.

Table 5-9. Early Childhood Development Program: Estimated Costs, Resources, and Financing Gap, Philippines, 1994–99
(*millions of pesos*)

	Health	Nutrition	Education	Total
Total resources required	7,128	6,793	4,937	18,857
Available resources	4,433	2,951	1,451	8,835
Resources as a percentage of cost	62	43	29	47
Financing gap	2,695	3,842	3,486	10,023
Magna carta gap[a]	774	394	0	1,168
Remaining gap	1,922	3,448	3,486	8,855
Financing gap (millions of dollars)	96	137	124	358

a. See the note to Table 5-4.

Source: World Bank and ADB data. See Section K of the supplement volume.

Finally, the financing requirements are heavily weighted toward recurrent costs, which make up more than 85 percent of the total. There are three main reasons for this. First, as will be discussed, ECD interventions are in their nature recurrent cost-intensive. Second, the need for erecting buildings is minimized through the proposed use of the barangay day care center as the convergence point for all three subsectoral programs. Third, construction costs are minimized through the proposed use of local materials for day care centers. The cost of building and renovating day care centers, in fact, makes up more than half of the capital costs of the investment program; if it were possible to rent suitable accommodations in some areas, the recurrent cost-intensiveness of the program could rise still further.

Sourcing and Sustaining the Financing

What are the recurrent cost implications of a strengthened national ECD program, and who should pay for it? To answer these questions we consider in turn the structure and build-up of the financing gap, potential financers of the program, the need to develop a cost-sharing policy, and the data required to develop such a policy.

Structure and Build-up of the ECD Program Financing Gap

Although all ECD expenditures are properly regarded as human resource investments in an economic sense, in a financial sense ECD expenditures divide into a mix of one-time capital costs and recurrent operational costs (particularly as repeated expenditures have to be made in order to invest in successive generations of children). In fact, ECD program interventions are by nature recurrent cost-intensive, because for the most part they consist of workers' salaries, drugs and vaccines, food and micronutrient supplements, educational materials, and in-service training. Such costs make up about 80 percent of the "remaining" gap. The capital costs for strengthening the ECD program consist mostly of the costs of establishing new day care and home-based centers, which make up about 80 percent of capital costs; the costs of replacing cold chain equipment are the other significant capital cost.

On the basis of the assumptions and estimates made above, the financing gap for the ECD program would build up quite rapidly over six years to a requirement of about ₱2.36 billion (about $84 million) in year six (Table 5-10). Of the "remaining" gap of ₱8.85 billion ($316 million) in 1999, about 95 percent would be recurrent

Table 5-10. Estimated Build-up of the Financing Gap of the Early Childhood Development Program, Philippines, 1994–99
(millions of pesos)

	1994	1995	1996	1997	1998	1999	Total
Health	446	456	409	451	472	461	2,695
Nutrition	0	423	615	760	903	1,142	3,842
Education	311	487	552	693	688	755	3,486
Total	757	1,367	1,576	1,904	2,063	2,357	10,023
Magna carta gap[a]	0	223	228	234	238	244	1,168
Remaining gap	757	1,143	1,347	1,670	1,825	2,113	8,855

a. See the note to Table 5-4.

costs, because the bulk of capital investment would already have taken place by the sixth year of the program.

The recurrent costs of the program would continue to rise until year six, simply because of the assumption made that investment in system expansion for PEM and early education would be spread over six years. After full coverage is reached in year six, recurrent costs should begin to fall. The main reasons for the anticipated fall would be, first, reduced costs for the immunization program (the largest element of health costs; see Table 5-4) as neonatal tetanus and polio were eliminated and, second, reduced supplementary feeding costs (the largest element of nutrition costs, see Tables 5-6 and 5-7) as the prevalence of PEM declined. However, it is difficult to quantify how great and how fast this decline would be. As an estimate for planning purposes, assume that the incremental recurrent cost burden of the ECD program over existing expenditures would be ₱1.5 billion to ₱2 billion ($54 million to $71 million) a year for five to ten years. Given the difficult fiscal situation in the Philippines, costs in this range mean that issues of financing and sustainability will be of paramount policy importance.

Who Should Pay?

This section reviews in theoretical terms the potential financing contributions of service users, NGOs, local governments, the central government, and donors from the standpoints of ability and willingness to pay, as well as equity and sustainability. It also suggests what the government would need to consider in developing a cost-sharing policy for ECD.

SERVICE USERS. Although government financing of ECD programs is strongly justified on cost-benefit and social welfare arguments (Chapter 1), contributions from users are desirable both to ease the financing burden on government and to increase users' ownership of the program. There appear to be no available data on users' ability and willingness to pay for ECD programs, and it would therefore be important to use the proposed client consultation process (Chapter 4) to find out more about this. It is known that users make small contributions to the materials and salary costs of running day care centers. But the lack of materials in most centers suggests that these contributions fall far short of targets, and answers to inquiries on field visits indicate that day care workers are often the main providers of teaching materials, from their own pay.

With better community mobilization, and with better-trained workers and higher-quality services on offer, users' willingness to make a financial contribution for services would probably increase. But it should also be remembered that the strengthened nutrition and early education services that form the bulk of proposed program costs would be targeted on the poorest—on families with malnourished children and on the poorest third of the barangay in the case of the day care program. Ability to pay among this group would therefore be very limited, and seeking significant contributions from them would quickly become regressive. Future contributions from service users are likely to rise at the same pace as the general alleviation of poverty. Substantial financing contributions from users are therefore likely to emerge in the long term, rather than the medium term, as the poorest become less poor. Currently, it would seem appropriate to explore the imposition of nominal user charges, with the aim of increasing users' involvement in the program and the program's accountability to users rather than with the aim of cost recovery.

NGOs. As with users, there are no data on the financing of NGO contributions to the ECD program. But NGOs' ability to substantially expand their project coverage from their own resources is likely to be extremely limited, because they depend on user charges and charitable contributions. Although a very large number of NGOs are involved in early education on a sustained basis, their work is sustainable either because they are serving a better-off clientele with the ability to pay or because they use fees from better-off clients to cross-subsidize poorer clients. Better-off clients are more plentiful in the urban areas, and it is doubtful whether NGOs can significantly increase their services in rural areas through self-financing.

It would therefore seem appropriate to use public funds to help NGOs expand their activities as community mobilizers and providers of good-quality services (see Chapter 4), rather than to look to NGOs as a significant source of funds. Cost-sharing arrangements with NGOs should be developed, as they have been in the Community Health Partnership scheme (described in Chapter 4), so that government resources do not substitute for contributions that NGOs would otherwise have made.

BARANGAYS AND LOCAL GOVERNMENTS. Although the implementation role of barangays and local governments after devolution is clear, policy with regard to the financing role of local governments in social sector programs after devolution is still being developed. Once again, the lack of data on ability and willingness to pay constrains the government's ability to develop an appropriate policy. And the very large variation in local governments' ability and willingness to pay makes policy formulation all the more difficult. Nevertheless, it is possible to make certain generalizations as a broad framework for policy development.

At the time of devolution, Internal Revenue Allotments (IRAs) to local governments were made on the basis of a political consensus to increase the total share of resources going to local governments. But although there was an attempt to ensure that the aggregate increase in IRAs for all local governments was more than enough to pay for the costs of all national services devolved to local governments, in practice the specific IRA shares of individual local governments often did not correspond well with the cost of devolved services to be absorbed by the local government. In fact, provinces and municipalities took on much higher costs of devolved functions in relation to their increased IRA share than did cities and barangays. Because cities were already paying for most health and welfare services before devolution, their additional IRA shares have been more available for other purposes, aside from just maintaining devolved services. Because barangays ended up with expanded IRA shares without corresponding cost assignments for devolved functions, their resources are also free for new initiatives. Many provinces and municipalities, however, are already facing difficulties in maintaining funding for devolved services at levels set by the national government before devolution. Their capacity to finance expansion or improved services is extremely limited in the medium term. This has important implications. If the case for substantial additional ECD funding is accepted, the financial situation of most provinces and municipalities after devolution will not allow them to pay the full costs of a strengthened program. If the case made here for government financing of ECD is accepted, then a substantial proportion of this funding would need to come from central sources, and the central government would need to develop a financing policy that would take into account differences in the local governments' ability and willingness to pay.

It is possible to conceive of a set of differing financing approaches for local governments with differing characteristics. At one extreme of the spectrum are very poor municipalities, with large populations in relation to their revenue base and very bad ECD indicators. Having inherited an inadequate infrastructure and budget and with little capacity to earn revenue, such local governments have no prospect of financing a strengthened and expanded ECD program from their own resources, even if they wish to do so. Because the 1991 devolution was not designed to correct for existing inequities in infrastructure and access to services, it would now seem appropriate for the central government to finance a large share of incremental program expenditures and then gradually reduce its share as the local government's ability to pay increased over time. At the same time, public policy must recognize that the local government's ability to pay cannot grow fast enough to absorb more than a portion of recurrent program costs at the end of six years. In this case, there is a rationale for continued central government subvention to sustain ECD activities over the medium and long terms on cost-benefit, externality, and equity grounds.

At the other extreme might be the well-off city that is able to pay most of the costs of an expanded ECD program but chooses not to do so in favor of spending on other sectors. Because of the national importance of the ECD program, it would seem appropriate for the central government to use advocacy, including cost-effectiveness data, to persuade the local government to invest in the sector, and to offer matching funds as a means of encouragement. At the same time, central funding should be conditional on the local government's significantly increasing over time its share of total spending going to ECD so that central spending did not simply substitute for the local government's obligations.

Most local governments in the Philippines fall between these extremes, having some understanding of the value of ECD investment, although an imperfect concept of what ECD entails, and having a significant ability to cost-share on an increasing basis over time, although not enough resources to pay for a strengthened and expanded program in the short term. Here it would seem appropriate to divide these local governments into different wealth classes and to decide, for each wealth class, an appropriate year-one cost share, year-six cost share, and rate of increase in cost-sharing. A fairly simple matrix showing changing cost shares over time by wealth class could be developed, which could then become a uniform and transparent basis for financing negotiations between central and local governments. However, local governments would need to be convinced that the basis of such a cost-sharing matrix was equitable, and this would require better data on ability to pay.

Aside from directly financing the costs of ECD interventions, local governments could also be the agents for implementing ECD cost recovery measures involving user contributions, voluntary community contributions, and NGO contributions. If a local government's total ability to pay is defined in terms of its own actual and potential revenues, plus the extent of households with some means to pay for ECD services, plus the presence of NGOs with some capacity to finance ECD services, then it may be possible to define local governments' cost shares on the basis of their overall capacity to mobilize all these sources of financing.

THE CENTRAL GOVERNMENT. As indicated above, financing from the central government is needed to help meet the gap between estimated costs and available resources. The central government should fill a proportion of the financing gap in the short term while local governments' revenues and ability to pay grow. It should fill a large proportion of the financing gap over the long term for very poor local governments with very limited prospects for revenue growth. And it should provide matching financing to stimulate increased local financing for ECD and ensure that local governments that underspend reach a target level of spending on ECD as a percentage of their overall spending. The mechanism for implementing each of these roles would be the negotiation of the Child Development Program Agreements proposed in Chapter 4.

Unfortunately, it is impossible to estimate how much central financing is needed for ECD without empirical work on local governments' ability to pay. Assuming, for the sake of discussion, that central financing may be required to fill 60 to 80 percent of the financing gap, this would imply a need for ₱6 billion to ₱8 billion ($214 million to $285 million) over six years, or up to ₱1.3 billion to ₱1.8 billion ($46 million to $64 million) a year, based on the proposed program's sixth-year incremental recurrent cost requirements. The central government has several options for sourcing its contribution to the ECD program: line agency budgets within planned ceilings for ECD; reallocations within line agency budgets within the planned departmental budget ceiling; or increments to line agency budgets. The increments in turn could be financed from interdepartmental budget reallocation, external aid, or increases in overall government spending. Although additional government spending on ECD is strongly justified in cost-benefit terms, for macroeconomic reasons recourse to additional government spending may be difficult and should be a last resort after other options have been explored.

There is a sharp contrast between the likely ability to pay of the Department of Health and the Department of Social Welfare and Development. The Department of Health was several times the size of the Department of Social Welfare and Development before devolution and has had significant budget increases since devolution, leaving it with a 1994 budget of more than ₱7 billion. The Department of Health's Five-Year Investment Plan contains a tentative allocation of about ₱5 billion for ECD. The Department of Social Welfare and Development, by contrast, lost most of its resources at the time of devolution and has had only small budget increases since then; its 1994 budget of about ₱0.76 billion contained negligible expenditure for centrally financed investment projects, and its current budget ceiling will not permit significant investment in early education or in replacing resources lost to the nutrition program by the withdrawal of PL 480 resources. Financing of a strengthened ECD program would therefore imply a substantial increase in the Department of Social Welfare and Development's budget ceiling; whether this would also be required for the Department of Health is unclear.

The potential for sourcing increased resources for ECD from reallocation within government budgets is substantial. Manasan and Llanto (1994) calculated the potential for raising additional revenues for health, nutrition, and education through reallocation (as well as other measures, such as more effective tax collection, which are outside the scope of this book). Within departmental budgets, the measures they analyzed included a reduction in the overhead expenditures of the Department of Health's central staff and the imposition of user charges for hospital care (together yielding up to ₱900 million a year, some of which could be reallocated to ECD), and a reduction in the Department of Social Welfare and Development's administrative overhead (yielding up to ₱100 million a year). Across departmental budgets, there is the potential to reallocate more than ₱1 billion from the National Food Authority's generalized food subsidy. A very strong case can be made for reallocating these National Food Authority funds into child nutrition, because these resources are already allocated for nutrition but are not being effectively spent.

DONORS. It will take time for local government revenues to grow and absorb an increasing share of ECD program costs and for the central government to agree on and implement intra- and inter-departmental resource allocation measures. In the interim, the central government would be faced with a sharp increase in ECD program expenditures, which could be met partly through increased commitments of foreign aid. Most bilateral and multilateral donors have accorded increased priority to social sector investments in recent years. However, few of the major donors to the Philippines are currently allocating significant funds to child development, despite its high returns. If the government were to demonstrate high-level commitment to integrating, strengthening, and expanding the ECD program, a strong case could be made to the donor community to review their sectoral resource allocations and increase their support for ECD.

It would be desirable for increased donor commitments for ECD to contain as large an element of grant financing as possible. It would also be desirable for donor financing to be packaged on a consortium basis, in the form of a single large project in support of the national ECD program. This would assist the government in developing a consistent national ECD strategy and program. It would also have administrative advantages, which have become especially important in the managerially complex postdevolution context, because it would permit the central government to negotiate with local governments a single program (with built-in flexibility) rather than a fragmented set of projects following different procurement, disbursement, monitoring, and reporting procedures.

Data Requirements

Although the central government can begin to develop the framework for a central government–local government cost-sharing policy based on the general considerations outlined above, developing a specific cost-sharing matrix as a basis for negotiating agreements can be done only after more data are collected on what local governments currently spend on ECD, and how willing they are to pay for a strengthened ECD program. A desk review of existing data in this area is being carried out. This review is likely to conclude that existing data are inadequate. If so, the review's findings would be used to develop recommendations for the design of a field survey of ability and willingness to pay. This survey would need to be undertaken simultaneously with the development of detailed proposals for investments in the ECD program.

Conclusions

The Philippines is now spending about ₱195 ($7.80) a preschooler on ECD, an amount that without further investment will fall to about ₱150 ($5.90) a child as existing child survival projects come to an end and donor support for the PL 480 nutrition program is phased out. To achieve the national goals for children, it is estimated that the nation should be investing about $11 a child—an increase of about 40 percent. The total increment required over a six-year period is estimated at about ₱10 billion (about $400 million), with an incremental recurrent cost requirement of about ₱1.5 billion to ₱2 billion ($54 million to $71 million) a year for five to ten years.

Although responsibility for ECD has been devolved to local governments, most provinces and municipalities are not able to strengthen and expand their programs, because the funds devolved to them are essentially sufficient only to maintain their pre-devolution infrastructure and recurrent spending, which are inadequate. There is a strong case for continued central government support for ECD on the grounds of cost-effectiveness, market failure, and equity. However, it is essential to devise a cost-sharing policy that will ensure that support from the central government does not simply substitute for efforts that local governments and communities could otherwise make. Local governments should therefore be asked to pay for an increasing share of ECD program costs over time, as their revenues grow. The size of this share should vary with the local government's ability to pay and its ECD needs. Cities, which did well from devolution, can pay a higher proportion. But it must be recognized that there will be a need for long-term central support for very poor municipalities with bad ECD indicators if the ECD program is to be sustained over the medium and long terms.

Much of the central financing required of the Department of Health can be raised within planned departmental budget ceilings. The Department of Social Welfare and Development, however, would require an increased ceiling to finance the strengthening and expansion of the day care center program. Reallocation of resources within and between government departments could also free up substantial additional funds for ECD, if this is designated as a national priority. With the upcoming withdrawal of PL 480 support, a particularly strong case can be made for reallocating expenditures by the National Food Authority for food subsidies into an effective nutrition program for children. However, budget reallocations are politically difficult and will take time. Time is also required for local government revenues to grow to a point where local governments can sustain an increasing share of the ECD program. In the interim, foreign aid could help to fill the financing gap. The donor community is putting few resources into ECD; a strong case could be made for donors to substantially increase their commitments if the government decides that reorienting and strengthening the ECD program is a national priority.

Note

1. "Magna carta" is the name given by the government of the Philippines for a specific package of benefits that was awarded by the central government to health field staff, but that has not always been paid by the local governments after devolution.

Bibliography

The word "processed" describes informally reproduced works that may not be commonly available through library systems.

Abella, Carmencita, Jaime Tan, Norbert Hirschhorn, and Chris Hermann. 1991. "The Child Survival Program Mid-Term Evaluation." USAID, Asia Bureau, Washington, D.C. Processed.

Adair, Linda S. 1992. "Postpartum Nutritional Status of Filipino Women." University of North Carolina at Chapel Hill, School of Public Health, Department of Nutrition. Processed.

Adair, Linda S., and Ernesto Pollitt. 1985. "Outcome of Maternal Nutrition Supplementation: A Comprehensive Review of the Bacon Chow Study." *American Journal of Clinical Nutrition* 41: 948–78.

Adair, Linda S., and Barry M. Popkin. 1992. "Prolonged Lactation Contributes to Depletion of Maternal Energy Reserves in Filipino Women." University of North Carolina at Chapel Hill, School of Public Health, Department of Nutrition, and The Carolina Population Center. Processed.

Alano, Jr., Bienvenido P., Aurora S. Villarosa, Belinda P. Alano, Milagros F. Silva, Rhais M. Gamboa, and Antonio O. Periquet. 1993. "Cost Estimates of the Philippines' Mid-Decade Goals." Corporate Assistance and Resource Associates, Inc., Manila. Processed.

Balisacan, Arsenio M. 1993. "Design of a Poverty-Targeted Food Subsidy Program in the Philippines." Development Alternatives, Inc.; C. E. Virata and Associates; John Mellor and Associates; and the Asian Institute of Management in association with Chemonics International; Louis Berger International, Inc.; and Access Asia, Manila. Processed.

Barba, Corazon V., Adelisa C. Ramos, and Raymundo Celestino F. Habito, Jr. 1990. "Growth Monitoring: Interpretation of Growth Curves." Department of Health Nutrition Service, Manila. Processed.

Barker, D. J. P., ed. 1992. "Fetal and Infant Origins of Adult Diseases." *British Medical Journal.*

Barth, Gerald A. 1983. "Street Foods: Informal Sector Food Preparation and Marketing in the Philippines." Equity Policy Center, Manila. Processed.

Bautista, Victoria A., ed. "Public Administration Bulletin." University of the Philippines, College of Public Administration, Center for Policy and Administrative Development, Manila. Processed.

Beaton, G. H., and Rae Mortorell. 1993. *Effectiveness of Vitamin A Supplementation in the Control of Young Child Morbidity and Mortality in Developing Countries.* ACC/SCN Nutrition Policy Discussion Paper 13. New York: United Nations.

Behrman, Jere R. 1992. *The Economic Rationale for Investigating Nutrition in Developing Countries.* Washington, D.C.: USAID.

Bhargava, Alok. n.d. "Modelling the Health of Filipino Children." University of Houston, Department of Economics. Processed.

Bisgrove, Eilene Z., Barry M. Popkin, and Corazon Barba. 1991. "Profiling Infant-feeding Patterns in Cebu, Philippines." University of North Carolina, at Chapel Hill, Carolina Population Center. Processed.

Black, Maggie. 1991. *Philippines: Children of the Runaway Cities.* Florence: UNICEF, International Child Development Centre.

Bondad, Myra P., and Adelisa C. Ramos. 1990. "Systems Analysis of Operation Timbang." Department of Health Nutrition Service, Manila. Processed.

Bouis, Howarth E. 1990. "Evaluating Demand for Urban and Rural Populations in the Philippines: Implications for Nutrition Policy under Economic Recovery." *World Development* 18(2):281–99.

Bouis, Howarth E., Laurence Haddad, and Eileen Kennedy. 1992. "Does It Matter How We Survey the Demand for Food? Evidence from Kenya and the Philippines." *Food Policy* (October): 349–60.

Briend, Andre, and Abdul Bari. 1989. "Critical Assessment of the Use of Growth Monitoring for Identifying High-Risk Children in Primary Health Care Programmes." *British Medical Journal* 298: 1611–14.

Cervinskas, J., N. M. Gerein, and S. George. 1992. "Growth Promotion for Child Development: Proceedings of a Colloquium Held in Nyeri, Kenya, 12–13 May 1992." International Development Research Center, Ottawa. Processed.

Chandra, Ranjit Kumar. 1991. "Nutrition and Immunity: Lessons from the Past and New Insights into the Future." *American Journal of Clinical Nutrition* 53:1087–1101.

Chavez, A., and C. Martinez. 1981. "School Performance of Supplemented and Unsupplemented Children from a Poor Rural Area."

In A. E. Harper and K. Davis, eds., "Nutrition in Health and Disease and International Development: Symposia from the XII International Congress on Nutrition." *Progress in Clinical and Biological Research.* Vol. 77. New York: Alan R. Liss.

———. 1982. *Growing Up in a Developing Community.* Guatemala City, Guatemala: Institute of Nutrition of Central America and Panama.

Chavez, A., C. Martinez, and B. Soberanes. 1992. "A 24-Year Study of Well-Nourished and Malnourished Children Living in a Poor Mexican Village." In *Longitudinal Country Nutrition and Health Research.* Boston: INFDC.

Child and Youth Research Center. 1988. "Impact Evaluation of the Early Childhood Enrichment Program, 1983–1987." Quezon City. Processed.

Congress of the Philippines. 1986. "The Child and Youth Welfare Code: Presidential Decree No. 603 (As Amended)." Manila. Processed.

Dargent-Molina, Patricia, S. A. James, D. A. Strogatz, and D. A. Santz. 1994. "Association between Maternal Education and Infant Diarrhea in Different Household and Community Environments of Cebu, Philippines." *Social Science and Medicine* 38(2): 343–50.

Dawson, Susan, and Mila Mates. 1991. *The Application of Quantitative Research Methods (RAP) in the Investigation of Community-Based Health Management and Community Health Worker Sustainability in 12 Rural Villages, Panay Island, Philippines.* Iloilo Field Office, Philippines: Save the Children Federation (U.S.A.).

Doan, Rebecca Miles, and Barry M. Popkin. 1992. "Women's Work and Infant Care in the Philippines." Institute for Health and Human Services Research, Tallahassee, Fla. Processed.

Eveleth, P., and John Tanner. 1976. *Worldwide Variation in Human Growth.* International Biological Program 8. Cambridge: Cambridge University Press.

Florencio, Cecilia A. 1980. "Household Behavior: The Nutritionists' Perspective." In Hans Bingswanger, ed., *Rural Household Studies in Asia.* Singapore University Press.

———. 1987. "The Academic Achievement of Elementary School Pupils and Biological, Educational, and Familial Factors (Focus on Nutrition)." University of the Philippines, Department of Nutrition, Manila. Processed.

———. 1989a. *Food and Freedom.* Quezon City: University of the Philippines Press.

———. 1989b. "The Nutritional Welfare of Filipinos and the Philippine Food and Nutrition Program." University of the Philippines, Center for Integrative and Development Studies, Quezon City. Processed.

Florencio, Cecilia A., Azucena B. Limbo, Alma M. Jose, and Emiliana M. Manago, eds. 1993. *Food, Nutrition, and Health Promotion: Directory of Institutions and Resource Persons in the Philippines.* Quezon City: ASEAN.

Florentino, Rodolpho F., G. M. Villavieja, J. P. Boquecosa, and F. F. Bacos. "The Nutrition Situation in Metro Manila." Food and Nutrition Research Institute, Department of Science and Technology, Manila. Processed.

Fogel, Robert W. 1994. "Economic Growth, Population Theory, and Physiology: The Bearing of Long-term Processes on the Making of Economic Policy." *The American Economic Review* 84 (June, 3):369–95.

Garcia, Marito, and Per Pinstrup-Andersen. 1987. "The Pilot Food Price Subsidy Scheme in the Philippines: Its Impact on Income, Food Consumption, and Nutritional Status." Research Report 61. International Food Policy Research Institute, Washington, D.C. Processed.

Ghassemi, Hossein. 1992. "Supplementary Feeding in Programmes in Developing Countries: Lessons of the 1980s." *Asia Pacific Journal of Clinical Nutrition* 1:131–52.

Gillespie, Stuart, John Kevany, and John Mason. 1991. *Controlling Iron Deficiency.* ACC/SCN Nutrition Policy Discussion Paper 9. New York: United Nations.

Gillespie, Stuart, and John Mason, eds. 1994. *Controlling Vitamin A Deficiency.* ACC/SCN Nutrition Policy Discussion Paper 14. New York: United Nations.

Glewwe, Paul, and Hanan Jacoby. 1993. *Delayed Primary School Enrollment and Childhood Malnutrition in Ghana: An Economic Analysis.* LSMS Working Paper 98. Washington, D.C.: World Bank.

Goertzen, Donald. 1991. "Rural Development to Counter Communists: The Silent War." *Far Eastern Economic Review* 23 (August).

Greenspan, Allison. 1992. "Poverty in the Philippines: The Impact of Family Size." *Asia-Pacific Population and Policy* 21 (June).

Haddad, Laurence, and Howarth E. Bouis. 1991. "The Impact of Nutritional Status on Agricultural Productivity: Wage Evidence from the Philippines." *Oxford Bulletin of Economics and Statistics* 53(1, February):45–68.

Harmatz, Zvi. 1993. "Investment Strategy for an ORT/EC Community-Based Project, Province of La Union, Philippines." Organization for Educational Resources and Technological Training, Metro Manila. Processed.

Hernandez, Jose Rafael S. 1993. "Social Marketing Communications: Its Contribution to the Philippine Child Survival Program." Republic of the Philippines, Department of Health, Child Survival Program, Manila. Processed.

HEWSPECS (Health, Education, and Welfare Specialists, Inc.). 1994. "Early Childhood Development in the Philippines." Manila. Processed.

Horton, Susan. 1988. "Birth Order and Child Nutritional Status: Evidence from the Philippines." *Economic Development and Cultural Change* 36(2):341–54.

Information Nutrition Action Foundation, Inc. 1994. "Community Development to Combat Childhood Malnutrition in Urban Poor Communities." Manila. Processed.

Kelly, Alan, and John Kevany. 1994. *Maternal Anthropometry and Pregnancy Outcomes: A WHO Collaborative Project for Meta-Analysis.* Dublin: Trinity College, Department of Community Health and General Practice.

Klein, R. E., C. Yarbrough, R. E. Lasky, and J. P. Habicht. 1974. "Correlations of Mild to Moderate Protein-Malnutrition among Rural Guatemalan Infants and Preschool Children. In J. Cravioto, L. Hambraeus, and B. Vahlquist, eds. *Early Malnutrition and Mental Development.* Uppsala, Sweden: Almquist and Wiksell.

Knudsen, Odin K. 1981. *The Economics of Supplemental Feeding of Malnourished Children: Leakages, Costs, and Benefits.* World Bank Staff Working Paper 451. Washington D.C.: World Bank.

Krasovec, Katherine, and Mary Ann Anderson, eds. n.d. "Maternal Nutrition and Pregnancy Outcomes: Anthropometric Assessment." Proceedings of the meeting Maternal Anthropometry for Prediction of Pregnancy Outcomes held under the joint sponsorship of the United States Agency for International Development, MotherCare, Pan American Health Organization, and World Health Organization. Washington, D.C., 23–25 April 1990. Processed.

Lenniger, Beryl. 1992. *Nutrition, Health, and Learning: Current Issues and Trends.* Newton, Mass.: Educational Development Center.

Levin, Henry M., Ernesto Pollitt, Rae Galloway, and Judith McGuire. 1993. "Micronutrient Deficiency Disorders." In Dean T. Jamison, W. Henry Mosley, Anthony R. Measham, and Jose Luis Bobadilla, eds., *Disease Control Priorities in Developing Countries.* New York: Oxford University Press.

Loevinsohn, Benjamin P. 1993. "Setting Quantitative Objectives in Health Sector Programs: Lessons Learned from the Philippine Child Survival Programs." Republic of the Philippines, Department of Health, Child Survival Program, Manila. Processed.

Manasan, R. G., and G. M. Llanto. 1994. "Financing Social Programs in the Philippines: Public Policy and Budget Restructuring." Philippines Institute of Development Studies, Manila. Processed.

Maria, Manuel O. 1993. "The Field Health Services Information System: Its Role in Decentralizing Health Services in the Philippines." Republic of the Philippines, Department of Health, Child Survival Program, Manila. Processed.

Martorell, Ray. 1992. "Overview of Long-Term Nutrition Intervention Studies Carried Out in Guatemala, 1968–1988." *Food and Nutrition Bulletin* 14:270–77.

Martorell, Ray, J. Rivera, H. Kaplowitz, and Ernesto Pollitt. 1992. "Long-Term Consequences of Growth Retardation during Early Childhood." In M. Hernandez and J. Argente, eds., *Human Growth: Basic and Clinical Aspects*. Elsevier Press.

Martorell, Ray, and Nevin Scrimshaw. 1995. "The Effects of Improved Nutrition in Early Childhood: The Institute of Nutrition of Central America and Panama (INCAP) Follow-up Study." *The Journal of Nutrition* 25(45, April supplement).

McKay, H., L. Sinisterra, A. McKay, H. Gomez, and P. Loreda. 1978. "Improving Cognitive Ability in Chronically Deprived Children." *Science* 200:270–78.

Mingat, Alain, and Jee-Peng Tan. 1995. "Do Preschool Programs Improve Elementary School Outcomes? Evidence from the Philippines." World Bank, Human Development Department, Washington, D.C. Processed.

Mora, J. O., M. G. Herrera, and S. G. Sellers. 1981. "Nutrition, Social Environment, and Cognitive Performance of Disadvantaged Colombian Children at Three Years." In *Nutrition in Health and Disease and International Development*. Symposia from the 12th International Congress on Nutrition. New York: Alan R. Liss.

Myers, R. G. 1992. *The Twelve Who Survive*. London and New York: Routledge.

National Task Force on Social Mobilization/Partners in Research, Training, and Community Organization. n.d. "A Review of Existing Policy Statements and Legislation Related to Child Survival and Development." Processed.

Nutrition Foundation, Inc. 1993. "Joint Micronutrient Mission to the Philippines: A Needs Assessment and Policy Formulation Experiment to Improve Micronutrient Malnutrition." Submitted to the USAID, Office of Nutrition, Washington, D.C. Processed.

Orihuela-Egoanil, Emilia. 1993. "Programmes de Nutrition en Milieu Rural aux Philippines." *Social Science and Medicine* 37(8):995–1003.

Pearson, Roger. 1995. *Thematic Eradication of UNICEF Support to Growth Monitoring*. Evaluation and Research Working Paper 2. New York: UNICEF.

Pelletier, David. 1994. "The Relationship between Child Anthropometry and Mortality in Developing Countries: Implications for Policy, Programs, and Future Research." *The Journal of Nutrition* 124(105, October supplement):2047s–2081s.

Pelletier, David L., E. A. Frongillo, D. G. Schroeder, and J. P. Habicht. 1994a. "The Effects of Malnutrition on Child Mortality in Developing Countries." Cornell University, Cornell Food and Nutrition Policy Program, Ithaca, N.Y. Processed.

_____. 1994b. "A Methodology for Estimating the Contribution of Malnutrition to Child Mortality in Developing Countries." *The Journal of Nutrition* 124(105, October supplement):2106s–2122s.

Pelletier, David L., and Roger Shrimpton. 1994. "The Role of Information in the Planning, Management, and Evaluation of Community Nutrition Programmes." *Health Policy and Planning* 9(2): 171–84.

Perlas, Leah, M. D. Kuizon, R. T. Tajaon, and J. A. Desmacido. 1992. "Iron Status of Pregnant Filipino Women as Measured by Serum Ferritin." *Southeast Asian Journal of Tropical Medicine and Public Health* 23(4):691–97.

Philippine Institute of Development Studies. 1993. "A Strategy to Fight Poverty." Paper prepared for the Presidential Commission to Fight Poverty. Manila. Processed.

Philippines, Government of the. n.d. "Directory of Non-Government Organizations in the Philippines." National Economic and Development Authority. Manila. Processed.

_____. 1991. *Education for All: A Philippine Plan of Action 1991–2000*. Vol. 1, Plan Document; Vol. 2, Programs and Projects. Manila: The National Committee on Education for All.

_____, Council for the Welfare of Children. 1993. "Data on Children." Manila. Processed.

_____, _____. n.d. "The Filipino Children: 2000 and Beyond, Philippine Plan of Action for Children." Manila. Processed.

_____, Department of Health. 1991a. *Integrating Services for Mothers and Children*. Manual No. 1: General Guidelines. Manila: Department of Health, Child Survival Program.

_____, _____. 1991b. *Process-Oriented Management Reporting System for the Partnership for Community Health Development*. Implementation Manual, 1st ed. Manila: Community Health Service.

_____, _____. n.d. "DOH Nutrition Polices and Strategies 1992–1996." Manila. Processed.

_____, _____. n.d. "DOH Plan of Action for the Survival, Development, and Protection of Philippine Children." Manila. Processed.

_____, _____, Nutrition Service. 1990. *A Compilation of Abstracts of Studies and Researches.* Manila: Department of Health and Helen Keller International.

_____, _____, _____. 1991. "Community-Based Planning and Management of Nutrition Program. Rural Health Unit, Trainer's Guide—Modules 4–7." Manila. Processed.

_____, Department of Social Welfare and Development. n.d. "Guidelines for the Local Government Units in the Formulation of Social Welfare and Community Development Plans, Policies, and Programs at the Local Level." Manila. Processed.

_____, FNRI (Food and Nutrition Research Institute), Department of Science and Technology. 1994. "The Nutritional Status of Filipino Children Using the International Growth Reference." Manila. Processed.

_____, _____. Annual. *Annual Report.* Manila.

_____, Food and Nutrition Research Institute, Department of Science and Technology, and Enfants et Developpement. 1989. "Nutrition Survey of Selected Depressed Barangays in Navotas, Metro Manila." Manila. Processed.

_____, National Nutrition Council. 1987. "Philippine Food and Nutrition Program." Metro Manila. Processed.

_____, _____. 1993a. "NNC Infokit." Makati, Metro Manila. Processed.

_____, _____. 1993b. "Philippine Plan of Action for Nutrition: Medium-Term Philippine Food and Nutrition Plan (1993–1998)." Metro Manila. Processed.

_____, National Statistics Office. 1994. "Philippines National Safe Motherhood Survey 1993." Draft report. Demographic and Health Surveys, Macro International. Manila. Processed.

Philippines, Government of the, and UNICEF. 1992. "Programme of Cooperation for Child Survival, Protection, and Development in the Philippines—Master Plan of Operations between the Government of the Philippines and UNICEF 1994–1998." Manila. Processed.

_____. 1993a. "Filipino Children at the Crossroads: Opportunities for Funding." Manila. Processed.

_____. 1993b. "Summary—Programme of Cooperation for Child Survival, Protection, and Development in the Philippines 1994–1998." National Economic and Development Authority and United Nations Children's Fund, Manila. Processed.

_____. 1993c. "Summary—Situation Analysis: Children and Women in the Philippines, 1992." National Economic and Development Authority and United Nations Children's Fund, Manila. Processed.

_____. 1994. "Terminal Implementation Review—Third Programme of Cooperation between the Government of the Philippines and UNICEF 1988–1993 (CPC III) Synthesis Report." Manila. Processed.

Pinstrup-Andersen, Per, Susan Burger, Jean-Pierre Habicht, and Karen Peterson. 1993. "Protein-Energy Malnutrition." In Dean T. Jamison, W. Henry Mosley, Anthony R. Measham, and Jose Luis Bobadilla, eds., *Disease Control Priorities in Developing Countries*. New York: Oxford University Press.

Pinstrup-Andersen, Per, David L. Pelletier, and Harold Alderman. 1995. *Child Growth and Nutrition in Developing Countries: Priorities for Action*. Ithaca, N.Y.: Cornell University Press.

Pollitt, Ernesto. 1991. *Malnutrition and Infection in the Classroom*. New York: United Nations Educational, Scientific, and Cultural Organization.

Pollitt, Ernesto, K. S. Gorman, P. L. Engle, Ray Martorell, and J. Rivera. 1993. "Early Supplementary Feeding and Cognition." *Monographs of the Society for Research in Child Development* 58(7).

Popkin, Barry, L. S. Adair, J. S. Akin, Robert Black, John Briscoe, and Wilhelm Flieger. 1990. "Breast-Feeding and Diarrheal Morbidity." *Pediatrics* 86:874.

Quisumbing, Maria Agnes R. n.d. "The Effects of Food Price and Income Policies on the Nutrition of Low-Income Groups: A Philippine Case Study." Paper submitted to the United Nations University Taskforce on the Impact of Agricultural Food Supply Policies on Nutrition and Health Status, Quezon City. Processed.

Raneses, Nestor O., Ferdinand G. Manegdeg, and Adelisa C. Ramos. 1990. "An Operations Research and Systems Analysis Study of Weighing Scales Used for Growth Surveillance (Operation Timbang) and Monitoring Program." Department of Health, Nutrition Service. Manila. Processed.

Salvosa-Loyola, Carmencita, and Adelisa C. Ramos. 1990. "Improving the Midwife's Performance in Measuring and Recording Body Weights of 0–6 Year Old Preschoolers." Department of Health, Nutrition Service. Manila. Processed.

Save the Children (U.S.A.). 1993. "Workplace-Related Childcare Services, Philippines." Philippines Field Office, Manila. Processed.

Schweinhart, L. J., and David P. Weikart. 1993. *Significant Benefits: The High/Scope Perry Preschool Study through Age 27*. Monograph. Ypsilanti, Mich.: High/Scope Press.

Scrimshaw, Nevin. 1995. "The New Paradigm of Public Health Nutrition." *American Journal of Public Health* 85(5):622–24.

Sebastian, Roberto S. 1992. "Rejoinder to the Global Nutrition Challenge: Lessons and Issues in the Philippines." Country statement to the International Conference on Nutrition, Rome. Department of Agriculture, Manila. Processed.

Selowsky, Marcelo. 1981. "Nutrition, Health, and Education: The Economic Significance of Complementarities at an Early Age." *Journal of Development Economics* 9(3):331–46.

Senauer, Benjamin, Marito Garcia, and Elizabeth Jacinto. 1988. "Determinants of the Intrahousehold Allocation of Food in the Rural Philippines." *American Journal of Agricultural Economics* 70(1): 170–79.

Senauer, Benjamin, and Marito Garcia. 1991. "Determinants of the Nutrition and Health Status of Preschool Children: An Analysis with Longitudinal Data." *Economic Development and Cultural Change* 39 (2, January).

Solter, Steven L. 1993a. "Area/Program-Based Health Planning in the Philippines." Department of Health, Child Survival Program, Manila. Processed.

————. 1993b. *Paying for Performance: An Approach to Donor Funding in the Philippines.* Manila: Department of Health, Child Survival Program.

Sommerfelt, A. G., and M. K. Stewart. 1994. *Children's Nutrition Status.* Demographic and Health Surveys Comparative Studies 12. Calverton, Md.: Macro International, Inc.

Taguiwalo, Mario M. 1992. *Implementing the Philippine Child Survival Strategy.* Manila: Department of Health, Child Survival Program.

Tan, Jee-Peng, Julia Land, and Paul Coustere. Forthcoming. "Putting Inputs to Work in Elementary Schools: What Can Be Done in the Philippines?" *Economic Development and Cultural Change.*

Tan, Michael Lim. 1992. "Philippine Health Matters 1992— Women's Health in the Philippines: A Critical Analysis." In *Health Alert.* Vol. VIII, special issue 129/130:1–40.

Tuazon, Maria, J. M. van Raaij, J. G. Hautuast, and C. V. Barba. 1987. "Energy Requirements of Pregnancy in the Philippines." *The Lancet* 14(November):1129–33.

UNICEF. 1991. "Nutritional Status of Filipino Pre-School Children Using NCHS Values 1987." Manila. Processed.

————. 1993. "1995 Mid-Decade Goals for Filipino Children, A Call to Action towards Philippines 2000." Manila. Processed.

————. 1994. "Goals for Children and Development in the 1990s: Achieving the Mid-Decade Goals of 1995, East Asia and Pacific Region." Manila. Processed.

UNICEF. Annual. "The Situation of Children and Women in the Philippines." Manila. Processed.

United Nations. 1993a. "Nutritional Issues in Food Aid." Papers from the ACC/SCN Session Symposium. Administrative Committee on Coordination, Subcommittee on Nutrition, Geneva. Processed.

———. 1993b. "Second Report on the World Nutrition Situation," vol. II. Administrative Committee on Coordination, Subcommittee on Nutrition, Geneva. Processed.

Villavieja, Gracia M., Wilma L. Molano, Corazon M. Cerdena, Ruby D. Lana, Elinita V. Castillo, Cynthia A. Nones, Josephine P. Boquecosa, Herminia SP. Abaya, Emerita A. Feliciano, Milagros C. Chavez, and Estrella F. Palafox. 1992. "1992 Update on the Nutrition Situation of Filipino Children." Nutritional Assessment and Monitoring Division, FNRI, Manila. Processed.

Waaler, Hans. 1983. "Height, Weight, and Mortality: The Norwegian Experience." *Acta Medica Scandinavica* supplementum 679.

Waterlow, J. C. 1992. *Protein-Energy Malnutrition.* London: Edward Arnold.

World Bank. 1990. "Colombia, Community Child Care, and Nutrition Project Staff Appraisal Report." Human Resources Division, Country Department III, Latin America and the Caribbean Regional Office, Washington, D.C. Processed.

———. 1991. "New Directions in the Philippines Family Planning Program." Report 9579-PH. World Bank, Country Department II, Asia Regional Office, Washington, D.C. Processed.

———. 1992. "Mexico: The Initial Education Strategy." Washington, D.C. Processed.

———. 1993a. "The Philippines: An Opening for Sustained Growth." Report 11061-PH. Country Department I, East Asia and Pacific Regional Office, Washington, D.C. Processed.

———. 1993b. *World Development Report 1993: Investing in Health.* New York: Oxford University Press.

———. 1994a. *Enriching Lives: Overcoming Vitamin and Mineral Malnutrition in Developing Countries.* Washington, D.C.

———. 1994b. "Philippines. Devolution and Health Services: Managing Risks and Opportunities." Report 12343-PH. Country Department I, East Asia and Pacific Regional Office, Washington, D.C. Processed.

———. 1994c. "Women's Health and Safe Motherhood Project." Staff Appraisal Report 13566-PH. East Asia and Pacific Country Department, Washington, D.C. Processed.

———. 1995. "Philippines. Social Safety Net Programs: Targeting, Cost-effectiveness, and Options for Reform." Country Department I, East Asia and Pacific Regional Office, Washington, D.C. Processed.

World Health Organization. 1985. "Energy and Protein Requirements: Report of a Joint FAO/WHO/UNU Expert Consultation."
WHO Technical Report Series 724. Geneva. Processed.

Young, Mary Eming. 1995. *Investing in Young Children*. World Bank
Discussion Paper 275. Washington, D.C.

Zohoori, Namrar, Barry M. Popkin, and M. E. Fernandez. 1991.
"Breast-Feeding Patterns in the Philippines." University of North
Carolina at Chapel Hill, Carolina Population Center. Processed.